Learning in the Early Years

Mathematics

Ann Montague-Smith

Activities based on the Early Learning Goals for under-fives

Ideas for planning, assessment and record-keeping

Photocopiable stories, rhymes and songs

Author
Ann Montague-Smith

Series consultant
Pauline Kenyon

Editors
Jane Bishop and Libby Russell

Assistant editors
Linda Forbes and Lesley Sudlow

Series designer
Joy White

Designer
Claire Belcher

Illustrations
Claire Boyce

Cover and photographs
Garry Clarke

Designed using Aldus Pagemaker
Processed by Scholastic Ltd, Leamington Spa

Published by Scholastic Ltd, Villiers House, Clarendon Avenue,
Leamington Spa, Warwickshire CV32 5PR

© 1998 Scholastic Ltd   Text © 1998 Ann Montague–Smith
67890   1234567

With thanks to Military Road Lower School in Northampton and Rainbows End Nursery in Leamington Spa for allowing us to photograph their work with the children.

The publishers gratefully acknowledge permission to reproduce the following copyright material:
Sue Cowling for the use of her poem 'Little frogs' © 1998, Sue Cowling, previously unpublished.
John Foster for the use of his rhyme 'Moving round the room' © 1998, John Foster, previously unpublished.
Qualifications and Curriculum Authority for the use of text from the Department for Education and Employment/QCA document *Early Learning Goals* © 1999, Qualifications and Curriculum Authority.
Karen King for the use of her story 'Timmy's rocket' © 1998, Karen King, previously unpublished. **Johanne Levy** for the songs 'Counting game', 'One, two, three sing to me' and 'Today's the day' © 1998, Johanne Levy, previously unpublsihed. **Tony Mitton** for the use of his poems 'Mr Wolf's morning'; 'Squirrel store'; 'How many?' and 'A tower of ten' © 1998, Tony Mitton, previously unpublished. **Judith Nicholls** for the use of her poem 'Short or tall?' © 1998, Judith Nicholls, previously unpublished. **Sue Palmer** for the use of her stories 'Luke and the ten pound note'; 'Fosbury's day'; © 1998, Sue Palmer, previously unpublished. Every effort has been made to trace copyright holders and the publishers apologise for any inadvertent omissions.

British Library Cataloguing-in-Publication Data
A catalogue record for this book is available from the British Library.

ISBN 0–590–53757–1

Contents

Introduction

Singing counting rhymes, sorting shapes and making patterns are all a regular part of life for under-fives. Learn to develop these interests into mathematical skills.

Children learn best through developing their problem-solving skills where a typical project might involve finding out how many bricks will make a tower as tall as themselves. These skills are integrated into the activities in this book with suggestions for questions for you to ask, which encourage children to set their own problems and find solutions. While children work they will be collecting data, such as the number of brothers and sisters they have, or who has a birthday today. Children will see pictures, words, symbols and numerals used at home, in books, in shops and on posters. It is important to use these in displays to show that they carry meaning. Developing mathematical language is also crucial to help children to develop their understanding about mathematical ideas. The activities in this book provide specific suggestions for questions you can ask to help children to think and talk about new ideas.

Early Learning Goals for Mathematics

Early Learning Goals	Mathematical content	Chapter
Children will be able to say and use number names in order in familiar contexts. They count reliably up to 10 everyday objects. They recognise numerals 1 to 9.	Counting Number	4 5
They use language such as 'more' or 'less', 'greater' or 'smaller', 'heavier or 'lighter', to compare two numbers or quantities.	Sorting, matching, comparing	7
In practical activities and discussion they begin to use the vocabulary involved in adding and subtracting.	Counting Number	4 5
They find one more or one less than a number from 1 to 10.	Counting Number	4 5
They begin to relate addition to combining two groups of objects, and subtraction to taking away.	Counting Number	4 5
They talk about, recognise and recreate simple patterns.	Pattern	6
They use language such as 'circle' or 'bigger' to describe the shape and size of solids and flat shapes.	Sorting, matching, comparing Shape and space	7 8
Use everyday words to describe position.	Shape and space	8
They use developing mathematical ideas and methods to solve practical problems.	Counting Number Pattern Sorting, matching, comparing Shape and space	4 5 6 7 8

The importance of understanding how children learn is covered in more detail in Chapter 2, where the development of mathematical language and problem-solving skills is considered, as are the expectations in preparation for inspection, the planning cycle, and planning to support adults working with the children.

The Early Learning Goals contain details of what young children should know, understand and be able to do in mathematics by the end of their Reception year. Some of the statements contain ideas about many areas of mathematics, while others are specific to just one area. The chart shows how the Early Learning Goals map into the activity chapters within this book.

Throughout this book the Early Learning Goals referred to are those published by the Qualifications and Curriculum Authority in *Early Learning Goals* for use in England. The ideas suggested here can be applied equally well to the guidance documents on pre-school education published for Wales, Scotland and Northern Ireland.

Planning

Planning to ensure curriculum coverage is discussed in Chapter 1. This includes:

* long-term planning, which shows curriculum coverage over one year;
* medium-term planning, which shows what will be covered during a term or half-term;
* short-term planning, which is the detailed weekly plan.

Such an approach to planning helps to ensure that there can be a developmental approach to learning, through returning to a mathematical idea in a different theme. It also satisfies the inspection requirements.

AUTUMN TERM	TOYS				
Jan-Feb half term. 6 weeks					
Personal and Social	Language and Literacy	Mathematics	Knowledge and Understanding of the World	Creative	Physical
Home area – Dolls' tea party	Rhymes – Miss Polly had a dolly Lists of toy words Story about toys	Toy sets Positional work with dolls' house Counting rhymes	Wheeled toys running down ramps Visit to toy museum	Art – Clay dolls Music – Repeating rhyhms Dance - Toys	Outdoor – Wheeled toys Indooor – Small apparatus Cutting with scissors

Mathematics should be part of an integrated curriculum, with mathematical ideas growing from any theme such as 'Toys'. In this way, mathematics will be integrated with the other curriculum areas of Personal, Social and Emotional Development, Language and Literacy, Knowledge and Understanding of the World, Physical Development and Creative Development.

All areas can be used to deliver mathematical activities. For example: children can be encouraged to count as they put shells on sandpies, pour cups of water into a bottle, make a tower of bricks, thread beads on to a lace, or plant seeds in a flower pot. This will encourage them to use their growing mathematical skills wherever they are working.

Equal opportunities

Girls and boys should both be encouraged to work at all the activities offered. Sometimes children have preconceived ideas about what boys do and what girls do, such as girls avoiding playing with construction kits because the boys are dominating the play there.

Through sensitive adult intervention you can encourage all children to

experience the range of provision and to become skilled in handling tools, working with construction kits, painting pictures, making models from clay and making exciting things to eat. Through these experiences girls and boys can be encouraged to develop their mathematical ideas and extend their mathematical language.

Second language learners will find benefit in developing concepts in both their home language and in English. Where possible, ask an adult who speaks the child's home language to work with her or him. This will help the child to develop the concept being taught in a particular activity through both languages.

Ensure your provision is suitable for children with specific physical needs. This could include providing sandpaper numerals for a sight-impaired child to learn to recognise by touch, or ensuring that an adult is available to help a child with poorly developed motor control. Children who are slower learners will need a structured approach to their learning, with perhaps very small steps planned to give them success. More able children will need to be challenged, perhaps by using larger numbers, or by finding alternative or improved solutions to problems.

Safety

Young children need constant and careful supervision. Be vigilant and try to anticipate hazards – if sand or water is spilled, clean it up immediately; do not allow a child to build a model in an unsafe place, such as behind the door and always keep the room tidy and clean. Ensure that the materials the children work with are suitable for the age range. Supervise the children closely when they are working with small or sharp objects.

Make sure that you are aware of any allergies, illnesses or other health considerations concerning the children.

If you are taking the children on an outing check the Local Authority regulations for the correct adult to child ratio and seek parents' permission.

Assessment and record-keeping

Detailed help with assessment and record-keeping is given in Chapter 3. Assessment is vital in order to help you to plan for the next step in a child's learning, building on prior learning. This can only be done if there is clear understanding about the developmental stages in mathematical learning and this is addressed through the activity Chapters 4 to 8, which, where appropriate, have activities in developmental order. In Chapter 3 there is detailed help with linking planning and assessment – through long-, medium- and short-term planning, on identifying when to assess, and on how to record. There are photocopiable assessment and record sheets on pages 73 to 76 to help you to keep track of the activities children have experienced, and their learning achievements, assessed on three separate occasions.

Working with parents

Parents can help their children to develop mathematical ideas by playing games at home, such as dominoes, snap, and board and dice games. These will particularly help with developing ideas about counting, quantity and numeral recognition. There are ideas for parent involvement within each of the activities in Chapters 4 to 8. Young children's mathematical learning is most effective when they are involved in practical activities. They need to play with resources, talk about their work, ask questions and find solutions. They may discover that 3 and 2 equals 5 through combining two groups of items and counting, but they will not understand formal addition and subtraction because they are not yet ready to work in the abstract.

Parents will enjoy helping their children to enjoy mathematics, especially when they understand how important it is to encourage practical activities at this stage.

How to use this book

This book can be used by the adults in any under-fives setting, including playgroups, nursery classes and nursery schools, day care centres and family centres. The activities described are suitable for all these groups regardless of facilities or group size. Resources which are recommended should all be readily available and you will not require any specialist equipment.

The book is intended to help you provide quality mathematical opportunities for young children and will help with planning, in any setting, and in preparation for inspection.

Help with developing the mathematics curriculum of your pre-fives setting is provided in each chapter of this book and the activities will help fulfill the requirements for inspection.

In the activity chapters the ideas use all areas, including movement, the music table, sand and water play, and stories, rhymes and songs.

Chapter 1 Planning – This chapter is specifically concerned with the how, what, when, and who in planning for quality mathematics.

Chapter 2 Child development – In this chapter how children learn effectively in each aspect of mathematics is covered.

Chapter 3 Assessment and record-keeping – Here help is given on how, what and when to assess.

Chapter 4 Counting – These activities help you to develop effective counting skills for your children; this is one of the most important aspects upon which so much future mathematical development depends.

Chapter 5 Number – These activities include early adding and subtracting, recognising numerals and recording numbers.

Chapter 6 Pattern – The approach to making patterns used here is through painting, music and using resources such as beads and laces.

Chapter 7 Sorting, matching and comparing – Here ideas of length, weight, capacity and time are developed, using everyday equipment.

Chapter 8 Shape and space – This includes learning about 3D and 2D shapes and their properties, and position and movement.

Photocopiable assessment and record sheets – Using these will help you to keep track of which activities children have experienced, and to keep good quality assessment records.

Photocopiable rhymes, stories and songs – These are integrated into the activity chapters.

Photocopiable activity sheets – These include games and opportunities to check whether children understand new concepts.

Recommended resources – This includes ideas for further reading, and other sources of activities for mathematics, equipment ideas and addresses for further information.

Other books in this series

All the books in this series will help you to deliver the Early Learning Goals and to be successful when inspected. The other titles cover:
* Language and Literacy;
* Personal and Social Development;
* Knowledge and Understanding of the World;
* Physical Development;
* Creative Development;
* Ready for Inspection.

chapter one

Planning

Planning for teaching and learning is essential to ensure quality provision. There are three stages to planning: long-, medium- and short-term planning. These are explained with suggested formats for written planning records.

Why plan?

You will need to plan carefully to ensure satisfactory coverage of the Early Learning Goals for Mathematics. This will enable you to check that children experience each aspect of the Goals and revisit them over a period of time so that their learning is secure.

Each child in your group has an entitlement to activities which address the Early Learning Goals and proper planning will help you to ensure that each child has the full range of experiences necessary by the time they are five years old.

Encourage all the adults in your team to take part in the initial planning process. This will help to give each member of the team a feeling of ownership about the work which they undertake, and to feel involved and knowledgeable about the purpose of each teaching activity.

Mathematics through play

Much of the mathematics that pre-fives learn comes through play. Set up the play environments such as sand, water or the role-play area with specially chosen resources to plan to provide specific mathematical opportunities in the children's play. This will be in addition to the activities which are planned as teaching activities. The combination of the two approaches will ensure a rich variety of mathematical opportunities for the children.

COUNTING		
Area	Activity	Resources
Snack time	Snack time count	Plates Raisins
Circle time	Action counting rhymes: (example from resources) Counting story	Copy of rhyme book
Table top toys	Hops and Leaps	Copies of photocopiable sheet xx Dice Shaker Counters
Gardening	Planting seeds - count out three seeds into the pot	Pots Compost Seeds Labels and pen Watering can
Book area	Counting pictures	Picture book Picture resource page xx Colouring materials

You may also want to plan for developing specific mathematical concepts or skills, such as counting. You can use the outcomes from the activities in this book to identify specific concepts or skills to be developed and to decide which environments you want to use and how to structure and resource them.

Parents and volunteers

Parents want to know what their children are involved in within your group and can be encouraged to extend activities at home. Suggestions for this are provided for each activity in Chapters 4 to 8. You might also consider producing a newsheet to display on the group noticeboard with suggestions for activities which can be tried at home.

Parents and volunteers may also help in your setting on a rota basis and they will need to know what has been planned, and what the main purpose of the activities are so that they can take a full part during their time with you.

Keeping records of planning

You will need to make written records of your planning. These are necessary to show everyone who works, or is a volunteer in your setting, the focus of the planned work. You will find it helps everyone involved if you keep the following records.

SPRING TERM			TOYS			
Week 4						
	Personal & Social	Language & Literacy	Mathematics	Knowledge & Understanding of the world	Creative	Physical
Monday 9.00	Home groups. News. Weather board.					
9.20		Book corner (Sam) Toys Story	Maths group (Jane) Teddy measures Comparing and Ordering by length: long, longest; short narrow Resources: teddies paperstrips scissors recording sheet	Cooking – gingerbread men	←— Cutting —→ and making and decorating own jigsaws	

The weekly plan

This can be displayed somewhere centrally so that all the adults involved have ready access to it. It will define the experiences required from each environment planned, and the resources that will be needed. It will indicate the learning outcomes planned for the week in question, and explain the role of each adult and where they will work at a given time.

It can be used to inform parents of the mathematical activities planned for their children during the week. This can be linked with suggestions for activities that parents can use at home to further extend their children's mathematical experiences.

Children's experiences

You will find it helpful to keep a record which shows children's experiences relevant to the Early Learning Goals for Mathematics. Record sheets on pages 75 and 76 are designed for this and can be used in a number of ways.

They can be used to record individual experiences; this is especially useful where children attend part-time and so will not have all the opportunities that a full week would offer. You can then check which experiences have not been covered by individuals and future plans can be developed to address these. These records can then be passed on with the children when they start school.

The sheets can also be used to record the experiences of groups of children. This will be particularly helpful where there are children of different ages and stages of development within each group. These can then be used to help you to plan ahead.

RECORD OF EXPERIENCES FOR MATHEMATICS: COUNTING AND NUMBER		
Name: Su-Lee Chan		
Counting	Learning outcome	Date
Circle time stories and rhymes	To recite the number names in order	Each week
Necklaces and bracelets	To make comparisons of quantity	Sept
Down on the farm	To count items which can be moved	Sept
Pennies and purses	To count the same items into different arrangements	Oct
Counting pictures	To count items which can be touched but not moved	Oct
Bird count	To count items which can be seen but not touched	Nov
Tambourine count	To count sounds	Dec
Hops and leaps	To count physical movements	Oct
Snack time count	To count out given quantities	Nov
Spin again	To count using counting skills in context	Each week

Building up records

Keep each week's planning sheet, perhaps taking it down from the noticeboard and placing it in a file. Over the weeks and months this will give you a record of what has been covered. It will help you to:
* evaluate the effectiveness of past planning and decide which aspects of that planning should be used again and which will need changing;

* check whether everything that was planned was covered;
* identify any gaps in planning and arrange to fill them;
* plan for the future to ensure that children have received their entitlement of delivery of the Early Learning Goals through a wide range of activities;
* provide evidence of what has been planned – especially important if there is any query about coverage of the Early Learning Goals and for inspection.

The planning cycle

Long-term planning

You will probably want to plan within a theme so that mathematical activities can be incorporated within all the environments in your setting. This planning may well include one or more of the other areas of the Early Learning Goals within an activity. Use the activity chapters to help you to decide on the balance of each of the areas of mathematics: counting and number; pattern; sorting, matching and comparing; and shape and space. There is an emphasis upon developing number concepts and skills in the Early Learning Goals, so try to ensure that during each week all children have opportunities to engage with number activities. Check that over a one-year-cycle all aspects of number have been covered sufficiently to meet the Early Learning Goals.

Ensure that your planning has sufficient breadth and that all aspects of the Early Learning Goals are covered over time, and that there is a balance between counting and number and the other aspects of mathematics. The importance of continuity, where new concepts and skills are introduced, developed and extended, and progression of topics within mathematics, where children are introduced to new ideas in an order that will help them to make sense of previous and new learning, are paramount in effective planning.

Medium-term planning

Develop this from your long-term plan and break it down into terms or half-terms. Use the activity chapters to help you to identify the learning outcomes for the mathematical activities and write these into your plans. Decide whether particular aspects of planning will be for all the children, or whether some activities will be for older or younger, or for the more or less able children.

Check that your planning includes the specific learning outcomes, which will help you to produce your weekly, short-term plans; indicates any activities designed for a particular group, such as younger or older children, children with special educational needs, or for individuals who may need a special programme; and shows balance between the emphasis upon counting and number and the other aspects of mathematics.

Short-term planning

Provide the detailed planning for each session in the coming week. Include timings so that all adults know when, why and what they are to do and details of resources needed. Plan for specific children including those with special educational needs, and plan differentiated activities for your range of age groups and abilities. In Chapters 4 to 8 there are ideas for every activity for working with younger and older children. Use these ideas to help you to plan.

SPRING TERM	TOYS
Long-term plan	Measuring length Counting rhymes Jigsaws
Middle-term plan	Comparing and ordering length: long, longer, longest wide, narrow, short Counting rhymes: numbers to 10 Jigsaws: fit together and take apart
Short-term plan	9.20 Maths groups: Teddy measures Comparing and ordering by length: long, longer, longest, short, wide, narrow, about the same, different Resources: teddies, strips of paper, scissors, recording sheet Blue group (older children) 11.00 Making each other's jigsaws to fit together and take apart Resources: jigsaws made previously Red groups (most able) 11.30 Counting rhymes: reciting numbers to 10 Resources: One elephant went out to play One, Two, Three, Four, Five, Once...

Check that your planning is clear to everyone so that all the adults in your setting can tell easily what is planned to happen; and that it shows differentiation, with appropriate activities planned for all ages and stages.

Supporting assessment

Build assessment into your plans. You will find that this will help you to ensure that you make worthwhile assessments for each child over time and to plan for individual needs.

In each stage of your planning, make sure that you have identified opportunities for assessment and the criteria that you will use. (The learning outcomes can be used as assessment criteria.)

• Long-term planning: check that there is coverage of all areas of the Early Learning Goals for mathematics.

• Medium-term planning: check where the assessment opportunities are for each area of mathematics and mark these on your planning sheet.

• Short-term planning: decide on a weekly basis what will be assessed, by whom and when. This is the detailed stage of planning for assessment.

From your weekly assessment plans, you will build up a picture of individual children's learning achievements which you can record on the assessment sheets on pages 73 and 74. This will help you to identify individual children who have specific learning needs and to plan suitable activities to support them during the coming weeks. For example, you may find that a child cannot count items beyond three or four. You can then plan some counting activities to help the child to develop their counting skills and plan to assess this again at a later stage.

During your weekly evaluation meetings (see page 14) discuss individual children and decide who should be assessed during the following week. Your assessment records will help you to check that everyone is assessed over a period of time.

Delivering the curriculum

It is important that all the adults working with the children share an understanding of what the Early Learning Goals mean.

The following notes are intended to help you to identify what each statement means in practice.

Children use mathematical language such as circle, in front of, bigger than and more to describe shape, position, size and quantity.

∗ Through your planning show that mathematical vocabulary will be developed through discussion about mathematical ideas and activities.

∗ Encourage the development of spatial awareness through movement sessions and handling objects.

∗ Provide opportunities for exploring properties of shapes and their relationships.

∗ Encourage children to describe clearly and precisely, for example explaining why a jigsaw piece belongs in a particular place in the puzzle.

They recognise and recreate patterns.

✳ Children should copy, make and describe patterns. They will be using resources such as shape tiles, beads and laces, sand and sand toys, painting and printing. They can also copy and make their own patterns through music and movement.

They are familiar with number rhymes, songs, stories, counting games and activities.

✳ Learning about the number system and how numbers 'work' forms the basis for future learning about number. Encouraging children to sing number songs and number action rhymes, and listen to stories which include numbers helps them to learn the number names and their order.
✳ Playing counting games gives children opportunities to use the number names in order and to count how many.

They compare, sort, match, order, sequence and count using everyday objects.

✳ Activities which include sorting and matching objects help children to use number language such as more, fewer and the same.
✳ Where children make comparisons these can be for length, weight, capacity and volume, so that they develop understanding about size and begin to order by size.
✳ Time involves very difficult concepts for young children, but they can begin to develop their understanding about sequencing events and ideas of fast and slow movements.

They recognise and use numbers to 10 and are familiar with larger numbers from their everyday lives.

✳ Counting and making comparisons of quantity, including handling coins, help children to use their growing understanding of numbers.
✳ They will see numbers used around them in everyday life, including large numbers such as those on prices and car number plates. They can begin to read and write numerals.

They begin to use their developing mathematical understanding to solve practical problems.

✳ Encourage the children to talk about and solve simple mathematical problems that arise from practical situations, such as when making models or sharing out drinks at snack time.

Through practical activities children understand and record numbers, begin to show awareness of number operations, such as addition and subtraction, and begin to use the language involved.

✳ This does not mean writing sums. It does mean using the language of addition and subtraction in every day situations such as 'If Sam eats two biscuits there will be five left.'
✳ Encourage children to record their mathematics, through pictures, making tally marks and writing numerals (see page 40).

Preparing for inspection

When your group is inspected, you will be evaluated against four aspects of the educational provision your group provides:

* the quality and standard of provision;
* the quality of planning and the content of your Mathematics curriculum;
* the quality of teaching and assessment;
* the effectiveness of your partnership with parents and carers.

Planning for teamwork

Planning is most successful when it involves the whole team who work with the children on a regular basis. These are the people who carry out the planning decisions and they need to be involved in this process so that they understand why particular decisions have been made. During inspection the adults' understanding of the planning process will be reviewed. To support the team try these three steps.

* Check that all the adults working with you know the focus for the day or week. They need to know which activities are offered and what learning outcomes are intended from planned teaching activities. They also need to know the purpose of any structured play, such as putting a bucket balance by the sand so that children can experience balancing with sand. This will help you to keep in touch with what everyone else is doing during the session.

* Hold short daily discussion sessions to evaluate the effectiveness of that session. Everyone will find it helpful to take part in this, and it is an opportunity to check that the planning for the next session is still appropriate. Weekly evaluation meetings should be held, when the events of the week can be discussed and the next week's planning finalised. A longer half-termly evaluation meeting, where the effectiveness of the planning of mathematical activities can be discussed in detail, is recommended. You can review the theme and whether or not it was appropriate for the mathematical concepts that you wanted to develop. This is also an opportunity to identify aspects of mathematics understanding that you need to develop yourselves.

* Having agreed that there are development needs for the adults, decide how these will be met, such as running a special evening where you could look at a range of activities and resource ideas for developing number, learning new songs and action rhymes, and trying out some new number games.

chapter two

Child development

**Understanding how children develop mathematical concepts
is an important element of successful teaching. Young
children will develop their understanding of mathematics
through play activities and by talking mathematically about
their work with adults and other children.**

Concept building

Children develop understanding of concepts and acquire skills through:
* experiencing practical activities, based on play environments;
* developing their mathematical language through talking about their work;
* exploring ways of recording using pictures, tallies and numerals;
* using symbolic methods of recording, such as writing formal sums and during Key Stage 1.

Developing mathematical language

Help children to understand and use mathematical language by:
* using the new language in discussion;
* encouraging children to use it so that they begin to understand its meaning;
* using a range of vocabulary to describe things or events, such as 'it's round, shiny...'; 'this has points and curves'; 'after we played on the swings we climbed up the climbing frame';
* encouraging the use of number language during conversations including counting numbers and 'more', 'fewer' and 'the same';
* using the correct language to describe a shape, so that children begin to discriminate between, for example, a cube and square.

Problem solving

The Early Learning Goals include developing children's skills in solving problems across all the areas of mathematics.

When you are with your group look for opportunities for children to:
* identify the problem: are there enough biscuits for snack time?;
* ask what if...? questions such as: 'What if we wanted one biscuit each? 'What if we wanted two biscuits each?';
* decide on the mathematics to use: share out the biscuits, one for you, one for you, one for you...;
* decide which equipment to use: biscuits and plates sufficient for everyone in the group;
* implement the plan: share out the biscuits, one at a time;
* discuss with others, using mathematical language: Are there enough? How many biscuits did we need? If everyone had two each, how many then? Do we all have the same number of biscuits?;
* evaluate the outcome: How did we do this? Was this a good idea? Was there another way? What else could we try?

Counting and number

Children learn to count by counting! It is no longer thought necessary for them to be skilled at sorting and matching before they learn to count, and instead, sorting and matching activities can be part of a counting activity. Young children can give instant responses to 'how many', of quantities up to 3 or 4, and this ability should be recognised and encouraged by the adults in the setting.

Skills for effective counting

The following experiences help to make children efficient at counting. They will need to experience each of these over and over again, using different resources, to develop their skills at counting:

* making comparisons such as more, the same...;
* learning counting names in order, for example, through singing number rhymes and listening to number stories;
* touching and counting at the same time, stopping the count at the last item;
* counting items which can be moved;
* counting items which can be touched but not moved, such as pictures in books;
* counting items which can be seen but not touched, for example wall frieze pictures;
* counting sounds such as tambourine taps;
* counting physical movements on board games or counting hops and jumps;
* counting and recounting the same items in different arrangements including lines, arrays, circles and random arrangements;
* counting out an amount, such as counting out enough biscuits for one each.

How numbers are used

There are three different uses of numbers, each of which children will experience in everyday life. Children gradually begin to discriminate between the uses and to understand what each entails. Cardinal numbers are used for quantity; ordinal numbers for order and nominal numbers as a name.

Exploring numbers

Numbers are in use all around us and children will see and recognise numbers in contexts, such as house numbers, posters on walls and on clocks and the television. They will meet larger numbers than those traditionally associated with young children and will enjoy learning their names and 'knowing' that these are large numbers. Their awareness of numbers can be developed through display so that children use data that has been recorded, and read and interpret it.

Some ideas include making a chart for prices in the café, putting a number plate on the pedal car, providing a telephone and clock in the role-play area, and listing ages and birthdays on charts.

You could display numeral charts to help children to recognise numbers in order and talk about larger numbers which children will see and hear in the environment. These will be in use at home, at the shops, on bus stops and as house numbers.

Beginning number operations

Young children learn about addition, subtraction and sharing through practical activities but they are not developmentally ready to do formal written arithmetic, as this is an abstract concept.

You can help the children to develop their skills with early addition, subtraction and sharing by setting up practical situations and asking them to solve practical problems, such as: 'There are six biscuits here. If Gary eats one how many are left?'

Encourage them to develop mental images of quantity by asking questions such as 'How many if we have one more? What if you eat one, how many then? I'll take two out, how many are left?' Some children 'see' the quantities in their minds and can use that to do simple addition and subtraction. Encourage finger counting to help them keep track. Children may discover for themselves that you can count on or back from a number to add or subtract.

They will begin to understand about sharing and that fair shares means everyone has the same. This is the early stages of understanding division and fractions.

Recording numbers

Some children will pass through developmental stages of recording by drawing pictures, then using tallies, and finally beginning to write numerals. Others may move from pictures to numerals. In your planning check that you provide many opportunities for recognising and writing numerals, such as writing on paper, in the sand, painting and cutting them out from magazines.

Pattern

Exploring sequences and patterns

Pattern ideas develop from understanding about 'nearness', and through language such as between, next to, in front of, and behind. Three-year-olds find copying patterns difficult. They gradually begin to separate out the elements of a pattern and to copy these, but not necessarily in the original order. They find it easier to copy the pattern if the original is placed above theirs, for example a threaded lace of beads on the table directly in front of them.

Older children may be able to copy a pattern, but will not make a reverse of it with accuracy. They cannot yet identify left or right and usually still put their shoes on either feet quite indiscriminately!

Discuss the order of elements in a pattern, using words such as next, first, last, in between and in front. Children will enjoy 'feeling' a pattern through art, music and movement, and repeating a sequence of movements or sounds to make a pattern.

Sorting, matching and comparing

Sorting and matching

These activities help children to identify similar, same and different. Encourage them to talk about their sortings so that they begin to understand that specific criteria and combinations of criteria, such as 'round and blue' or 'has wheels and it's made of metal' can be used. Sorting activities should include the 'not' category, so that children develop the concept that some things belong to a set and others do not.

Comparing

Young children find concepts of distance difficult and they tend to refer to familiar journeys as being shorter (or nearer) than unfamiliar ones. They believe that if something is placed between two items, then this makes the further item even further away. They will make direct comparisons of length, but not notice whether they have lined both items up. They will just look at one end, so should be encouraged to line up items to be compared.

They will have little understanding of conservation of any measure until at least the end of Key Stage 1, but they can begin to:
* compare and order for length, weight and capacity and use the relevant language;
* use a balance and understand more, less and weighs the same;
* understand about capacity that there is a difference between social 'full' and mathematical 'full', for example, we do not fill a cup to the brim or it will spill.

Exploring concepts of time

Time has two abstract concepts:
* measurement of time, such as using a clock or a calendar;
* the passing of time, such as the seasons, days, nights, birthdays.

Young children can begin to recall events, but these may not be in time sequence and they will have little understanding of periods of time such as a fortnight. Encourage them to make comparisons of time by using home-made sand-timers and recognising key times on a clock, such as home time.

Shape and space

What do children observe?

By about the age of three, children can discriminate between open and closed figures, but not between different types of closed figures, so their drawings will lack accuracy. From about the age of four their drawings become more recognisable, and show features such as points and curves.

Developing concepts of shape and space

Children learn about shape and space through practical activities, such as picking up and examining shapes, making models from building bricks and construction kits and taking them apart, and using shape posting boxes and jigsaws. You could provide a magnifier for examining small objects. Encourage the children to use everyday and mathematical language to describe what they see and make.

They will enjoy exploring lines and movement, through painting and sewing, and also through moving themselves in straight, zigzag and curved lines. Using a climbing frame helps children to understand movements of up, down, through, over and under. Use a computer toy such as Roamer, or screen software such as *First Logo* to explore position and movement.

Children will enjoy printing with sponges, cotton reels and corks, and will begin to recognise the shapes of faces of 3D objects. They can use mirrors to look at symmetrical patterns.

Encourage the development of observational skills by asking children to copy models from pictures and to draw their models. Ask them to compare the drawings with the models and their models with the original pictures.

chapter three

Assessment and record-keeping

Quality assessment which is used for planning is very important for children's learning. Planned assessment is part of the teaching programme so that it is manageable. Assessment records build up over time to give a clear view of each child's achievements and needs.

The importance of assessment

It is important to use systematic assessment, which will give a clear picture of each child's stage of development in all aspects of their mathematical learning.

You will find the developmental approach in the activity chapters will help you to assess achievements and to identify the next stage in learning. This will enable you to plan activities which will both extend the child's experience and build on the foundations of previous learning. It will enable you to show parents/carers, the child, and ultimately a new class or school how much progress he or she has made over time. This will prove the value of what your group has to offer and help you to evaluate and improve your work. It will also help, where progress has been very limited, in identifying children with special needs at an early stage so that they can receive appropriate extra help.

National Baseline Assessment

All schools in England and Wales are now required to undertake formalised 'Baseline Assessment' shortly after a child commences statutory age schooling. Schools must use a baseline assessment system that has been officially accredited by the DfEE, and there is an equal entitlement for all children, including those for whom English is an additional language.

Although baseline assessment does not apply to nurseries or pre-school settings, all settings must assess the children's achievement against the Early Learning Goals and these assessments could contribute towards baseline assessments for five-year-olds in school. Such assessments in mathematics will check the child's competence in:

* creating patterns;
* ordering objects by size;
* demonstrating 1:1 correspondence by matching item to item;
* identifying ordinal position (for example first, third, middle in a line of toys);
* counting objects accurately;
* recognising numerals;
* writing numerals;
* adding and subtracting using objects;
* solving simple numerical problems using addition and subtraction.

The child's development of mathematical language will be the key in this process.

Linking planning and assessment

For each of long-, medium- and short-term planning, you will need to check that the opportunities for assessment are identified.

Long-term planning

This is the planning for a year. Go through your long-term plan and highlight assessment opportunities with an asterisk. Check that all aspects of the Mathematics Early Learning Goals will be covered and revisited so that there will be opportunities to assess each aspect on more than one occasion.

> AUTUMN TERM
> 6 weeks
> BUILDINGS
> Mathematics
> 3) 3D shapes *
> Number rhymes

You may have new intakes during the year and will want to allow time for these children to settle before formal assessments are made. Also, consider whether the assessments will be for everyone, or for specific children. You may want to assess the older children's ability to solve practical problems and the younger children's skills with counting. If your long-term plans do not include sufficient opportunities for some aspects of the Mathematics Early Learning Goals, you can adjust your planning at this stage.

Medium-term planning

> AUTUMN TERM
> 6 weeks
> BUILDINGS
> Mathematics
> 3) Simple properties of 3D shapes – making models
> Number rhymes counting backwards 10 → 1

Transfer the highlighted assessment opportunities on to your medium-term plan. Check that all aspects are covered and that there is a spread of assessment opportunities. Assessment must not overload you, so check that the assessments to be made for each week will be manageable. It is not necessary to create special assessment activities. Make your own planned activities into assessment opportunities and asterisk these accordingly. Use the learning outcomes from the activities in Chapters 4 to 8 to help you to identify the activities which you would find helpful for assessment. For example, use 'Pictures, tallies and numerals' on page 40 to assess the children's ability 'to record how many'.

Short-term planning

As you prepare your short-term, weekly plans, take note of what assessment has been planned and make more precise arrangements for specific children to be assessed.

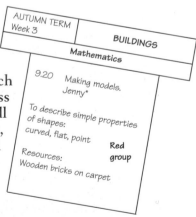

> AUTUMN TERM
> Week 3
> BUILDINGS
> Mathematics
> 9.20 Making models. Jenny*
> To describe simple properties of shapes: curved, flat, point
> Resources: Wooden bricks on carpet
> Red group

You will need to decide what will be assessed by identifying the learning outcomes of the planned activities and which children will be assessed – it may be that you want to assess everyone and so will need to plan when groups of children will be assessed, or, you may want to assess just a few children, perhaps the more able, the younger children, or an individual who you believe may have special educational needs. You need to determine when the assessment will take place and who will make the assessment, including these details in your planning for the week.

The assessment process

When to assess?

After an appropriate settling-in period, you will want to assess each child. The outcome of the assessment will give you information about their current stage of development in mathematics. In your planning, you can identify appropriate activities which can be used to make a baseline, or first, assessment across all aspects of the Mathematics Early Learning Goals.

You will also want to use your discussions of this first assessment with parents to plan, and they will also give you an opportunity to learn about the mathematics the child does at home, and to share targets together, for example: 'We are working on encouraging her to count to five.'

Mathematical skills				Name ____ Sam Brooks ____			
	Assessment comments						
Skills and concepts	Baseline/1st assessment	Date	2nd Assessment	Date	End of year assessment	Date
Can use mathematical language to describe: • shape • position • size • quantity	Uses words such as on, under, round, flat, big, small, more, same	2nd Oct	Makes models and describes shapes, eg curved, longer, shorter, on top, next, before. Counts how many to 7	5th Feb	Compares to find and describe heavier, lighter, full, empty. Counts out accurately to 10 and compares how many (more/fewer).	3rd May
Can: • recognise patterns • make patterns	Makes a threaded bead pattern. Does not copy a given one	20th Sept	Makes a threaded bead pattern. Does not copy a given one	12th Dec	Copies a given pattern. Makes simple ABAB pattern.	3rd July

You will want to make other assessments to mark progress. Decide upon what is manageable for your setting. The 'mathematical skills' assessment sheet (page 73) has three columns. You could use one column for each term, which would be easily managed.

The 'Counting to 10' assessment sheet (page 74) can be useful in helping you to check that individual children are confident in all the important aspects of learning to count. Using this sheet will also help you to identify those children for whom you need to plan further experiences in counting.

Counting to 10				Name ____ James Spencer ____			
	Assessment comments						
Skills and concepts	Baseline/1st assessment	Date	2nd Assessment	Date	End of year assessment	Date
Can recite the number names in order.	Counts to 5	8th Oct	Counts to 10	3rd Mar	Counts forwards and backwards to 10	9th June
Can make comparisons of quantity.	Knows more and same	10th Nov	Finds one more, one fewer	4th Feb	Makes sets of 'more than 6' 'fewer than 4' accurately	7th May
Can count items which can be moved.	Does not match touch and count	17th Oct	Matches touch and count to 6	19th Mar	Counts items to 10	27th June

Who assesses?

Assessment should involve all the adults, including parents and volunteers, who work with the child in your setting, as everyone will be able to make useful contributions. However, everyone should be clear about what is being assessed. Brief, written directions are useful to focus adults on the exact area for observation. For example, in assessing counting objects that can be manipulated, adults will find it helpful to check that children touch the object and say the counting number at the same time. Activities in chapters 4 to 8 include specific questions which will help to identify children's achievements.

Parents may wish to contribute towards their child's assessment record from observations made at home.

How can we assess?

When particular children are to be assessed during an activity, such as printing, the group leader will need to know:

* which children are to be assessed;
* that they should make a repeating ABAB pattern by alternating prints with a sponge and cork, for example;
* that they should encourage the children to describe their patterns;
* that this could be recorded on a dated tick list, or by making notes for later recording on the child's record sheets (pages 75 and 76).

Hannah Moore
Mathematics Record

15th Sept — She built a tower with bricks 'Lots and lots. More than Jon.' Her tower was taller than Jon's. Assess for comparing/ordering length.'

23rd Sept — Hannah counted. 'One, three, four, two, five.' More experience for counting needed – counting rhymes.

8th Oct — Hannah counted to 10 with all the numbers in order. She was thrilled!

You may also want to target two children each day or session for assessment on a rolling programme. Ask all the team to make a note of what the targeted children do, achieve and also what they say. Keep a page for each child in a file for mathematics. At the end of each session spend a few minutes making notes about them.

In this way information can be built up about each child's mathematical achievements over a period of time. This will help you identify any specific assessments that you need to make for individual children in order to build a more complete picture of their achievements. You can then build these specific assessments into your weekly planning, and decide when and by whom the assessments will be carried out.

How can we record?

The above assessment ideas will provide you with a record for mathematics for individual children and, together with completed 'Mathematical skills' assessment sheet (page 73) and the 'Counting to 10' assessment sheet (page 74), you will have a strong evidence base of what has been achieved. When the child leaves your setting these record sheets can be passed on to school as a record of achievement.

You may also want to keep examples of their work, selected over time, to show their achievements. These could include drawings, pictures, tallies, numerals, line patterns and print patterns made by the child. You could include photographs of models, or the children using mathematical ideas, such as when working with the dolls' house or the farm. This will build into portfolios of work for individual children. It is helpful to annotate and date each piece of work, to show which aspects of the Early Learning Goals are represented and the progress over time.

The assessment portfolio will provide a useful focus for discussing work with parents and carers, and they may like to contribute further evidence such as photographs of the child helping to sort the washing or put away the shopping. When the child leaves they can take their portfolio with them or it can be transferred to the school as a very valuable record showing attainment and progress.

Involving parents and carers

Parents and carers are the first educators and they should ideally be partners in their child's learning and fully informed of the work undertaken. Ideally, make contact before the child starts at your setting as they can share important aspects of their child's mathematical achievements. For example, they may know that the child can already count to five and complete quite complicated jigsaws unaided.

Arrange to discuss each child's progress with parents as soon after your first assessment as possible and set targets that you can both work on. Perhaps the child needs to develop 'counting things that they can see but not touch', and you can suggest how the parents can encourage them to count chimneys on roofs, or objects in posters.

Send home regular newsletters giving an outline of the work to be covered and let parents know how well their children are doing, showing photographs and drawings from their work.

chapter four

Counting

Effective counting is an essential part of learning about mathematics. We learn to count by counting, reciting the counting names in order and matching them to the items to be counted. The following activities include all the ingredients necessary to help children to become skilled at counting.

Circle time stories and rhymes

Learning outcome

To recite the number names in order.

Group size
Any size of group.

What you need
Action songs and rhymes chosen from 'Today's the day', 'A tower of ten', and 'Little frogs', pages 87, 79 and 78 or favourites of the children such as: 'Peter hammers with one hammer' or 'One elephant went out to play' which count from one upwards, and 'Five little speckled frogs' or 'Ten green bottles' which count down from five or ten.

Preparation
Prepare a space so that there is enough room for everyone to sit in a circle.

What to do
Ask the children to sit in a circle and explain that they will be singing some action number songs. Sing the chosen song to the children and show the actions, then ask them to join in as you sing it again. With finger-action rhymes ask children to hold up their fingers to show one finger, two fingers, three fingers and so on. Include songs which count backwards from five or ten so that they hear the counting pattern both forwards and backwards.

Questions to ask
What number comes after four? What number comes after ...? What number comes next? What number comes before ...? What number comes between ... and ...?

For younger children
Choose songs with a limited number range to two, three or four, such as 'Baa baa black sheep', and increase the number range as they become more confident.

For older children
As well as songs which count up to ten, use songs which count back from ten to one or zero. Ask the children to hold up their fingers to show how many each time.

Follow-up activities
∗ Sing songs which count backwards in twos, such as 'Ten fat sausages'.
∗ Tell stories about three or more people or animals, such as 'The Three Bears', or 'The Three Billy Goats Gruff'.
∗ Dress up as the characters in a number story or rhyme and act out the counting story.

Links with home

Ask parents and carers to encourage the children to recite the number names in order, forwards and backwards and to sing action number rhymes.

Necklaces and bracelets

Learning outcome

To make comparisons of quantity.

Group size

Four children.

What you need

Coloured beads, laces and a tray.

Preparation

Place the beads and laces on a tray in the centre of a table.

What to do

Ask each child to take a lace and a small quantity of beads and to thread their beads on to the lace. They count how many beads they have threaded. Thread a lace with some beads and show the children. Ask them to make their lace have the same number of beads as yours. Repeat the activity with different quantities of beads. The lace can be tied by an adult to make a necklace or a bracelet which can be worn by the child when dressing-up in the role-play area.

Questions to ask

Who has used more than three beads? How many more? Who has fewer beads than ...? Who has more than ...? Who has a different number of beads than this? Who has threaded the most beads? How many more beads do you need to make yours like this?

For younger children

Limit the number of beads to be threaded to three, four or five. Ask the children to count their beads, then to thread one more on to their lace and say how many they have now.

For older children

Increase the number of beads, up to ten. Ask the children to thread five beads, two more than five, three fewer than six. Repeat the activity with different quantities of beads.

Thread a lace with ten beads and ask the children to make their lace have the same number as yours. They can count how many more beads they have to thread.

Follow-up activities

* Put cars in the garage: 'three cars here', 'two more here'.
* Use hoops in movement sessions and ask varying numbers of children to stand in the hoops: for example, 'more than three'; 'fewer than five'.
* Play Snap and ask the children: 'how many more on that card are there than this one?'.

Links with home

As they clear away their toys children can count them by colour, and then decide which colour has more and which fewer.

Down on the farm

Learning outcome

To count items which can be moved.

Group size

Four children.

What you need

Toy farm animals, farm buildings and fields (pieces of green cloth or card).

Preparation

Ask the children to set up the farm on a table and put a field in front of where they will sit.

What to do

Invite each child to choose which animals will go in their field and to count how many they have. Encourage them to count and touch the farm animals at the same time so that they develop the idea that each counting number matches one of the items to be counted. After each touch they move that animal away from the others so that they can see which they have counted and whether there are any more to be counted. Repeat the activity with a different quantity of animals, gradually increasing the quantity over the weeks, up to ten.

Questions to ask

How many animals have you counted? Do you all have the same number? Who has more? Who has fewer? Who has the same as me?

For younger children

Limit the size of the group of animals to no more than five. As one child touches and moves the animals the others can count with them.

For older children

The children can compare how many animals they have with those of the other children. They can ask questions such as: Who has more than five? Who has fewer than eight? Who has the same number as me?

Increase and decrease how many animals they have by adding and removing one, two or three animals each time.

Follow-up activities

∗ At clearing-up time count how many pencils or crayons are on each of the tables.

∗ Throw a dice and count, touch and move that number of counters.

∗ Count out a given quantity of Multilink cubes and make a model using all of them.

∗ Make a pattern with pegs on a pegboard to match a given number.

∗ Make lines of sorting toys, Compare Bears for example: one; two; three... up to ten toys.

Links with home

At meal times, children can count how many knives, forks, spoons, plates and mugs are needed for the family.

Pennies and purses

Learning outcome

To count the same items in different arrangements.

Group size

Four children.

What you need

Pennies, purses or saucers, numeral cards, paper, pens.

Preparation

Ask the children to put ten pennies in the purses. Alternatively they can put the pennies on to the saucers.

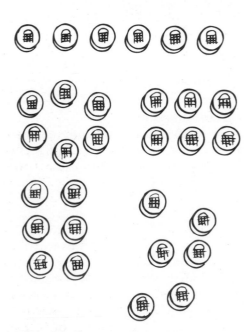

What to do

Invite each child to count out six pennies from their purse or saucer and put them down in front of them. Ask them to count the pennies again, then to put them into a straight line and count them again. Check that they count each penny in the arrangement just once. Then ask them to try other arrangements of the pennies, for example in a circle, each time re-counting the same pennies. (See diagram above.)

Repeat the activity for different quantities of pennies.

Questions to ask

How many pennies are there? How many pennies in the circle? How many pennies when they are in a straight line? Are there the same number of pennies?

For younger children

Use a smaller number of pennies, such as three, four or five. Ask if there is the same number of pennies each time they make a pattern. Repeat the activity again on a different day using one or two more pennies.

For older children

Repeat the activity over the weeks, gradually increasing the quantity of pennies to ten. Children can put a numeral card beside each arrangement of pennies to show how many or they can write the numeral for themselves. Ask each child to make an arrangement with their pennies which is different from the other children's. They can see how many different ways they can find using the same quantity.

Follow-up activities

The following items can be used to make different arrangements of the same quantity:

* pegs on a pegboard;
* shells in sand;
* buttons;
* pasta shapes stuck on to card;
* felt shapes;
* small bricks.

Links with home

Children can count clothes pegs, making different arrangements with them, and re-counting each time. They can arrange, count and rearrange small toys such as cars, dolls and construction kit pieces.

Counting pictures

Learning outcome

To count items which can be touched but not moved.

Group size
Four children.

What you need
A story or counting picture book with clearly defined groups of things which can be counted, photocopiable activity sheet 'Counting garden' on page 88, colouring materials.

Preparation
Copy the 'Counting garden' sheet and give one to each child to colour. Read the picture book story to the children before the activity begins.

What to do
Read the picture book story again with the children, and for each page ask them what they can see in the picture. When they have described some of the items, ask them to take turns to count the items, touching them as they count. Check that they count each item, but just once. When they are confident with this, they can use their copy of the 'Counting garden' sheet. Ask them to count the birds, the flower petals and so on. Encourage the children to check each other's counting. Check that they include everything in the group that they are counting.

Questions to ask
How many ... can you see? Are there more ... or more ...? How do you know? I can see four ... Can you point to them for me?

For younger children
Use pictures with fewer items to count, including one and two items. They can cover the pictures with counters as they count, to show which ones they have already counted.

For older children
Increase the quantity of items to be counted up to about ten in each group. Check that children count each item and only once. Introduce the idea of 'zero' or 'nothing' by asking the children to count something that is not in the picture.

Follow-up activities
∗ Count items in the children's own drawings and paintings.
∗ Count items in magazine and catalogue pictures.
∗ Count items in pictures on display where the children can touch them as they count.
∗ Play picture and number match card games, Picture dominoes and Picture lotto.

Links with home

When parents or carers read stories from picture books, they can encourage their children to count the items in pictures.

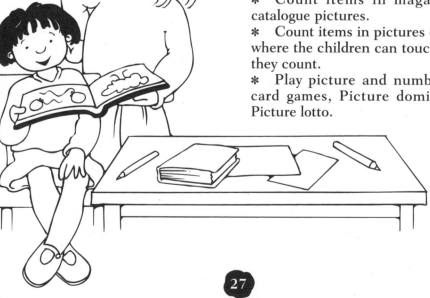

Bird count

Learning outcome

To count items which can be seen but not touched.

Group size
Four children.

What you need
A wall display area, card, paint or collage materials, Blu-Tack.

Preparation
On the wall display area, mount a large tree outline, with branches.

What to do
Ask the children to help to make birds, to put on the tree display. When these are finished they can be put on to the tree with Blu-Tack. They need to draw squirrels and other animals on or by the tree as well. Ask the children to stand near to the display and count the birds, then the squirrels and any other animals without touching them. Check that they count each one just once and that they count all of the particular group each time. They may find it helpful to point to each one as they count. Ask the children to count out loud as you remove the birds one at a time. This helps them to check that they have counted each one just once. Repeat the activity with a different quantity of birds and animals.

Questions to ask
How many birds can you see? How many now? Are there more squirrels or more birds? How many birds are flying? How many birds are in the tree? How many birds altogether?

For younger children
Use one, two and three birds at first and encourage the children to point to the birds, but not to touch them as they count. Remove each bird as they point and count until there are none left.

For older children
Ask the children how many more birds there are than squirrels. Add two more birds and ask how many more there are now. Ask the children to shut their eyes and put the birds in different places. Ask them to open their eyes, count the birds again and say if there are more, fewer or the same number as before.

Follow-up activities
∗ Count chimney pots on the roofs of houses.
∗ Count the trees in your local park.
∗ Count items on a piece of wallpaper.

Links with home
When out shopping with their family, children can count items in shop windows, or on advertising posters.

Tambourine count

Learning outcome

To count sounds.

Group size
Any size of group.

What you need
Tambourine or drum.

Preparation
Prepare a place to sit so that the tambourine can be hidden from the children's view. Ask the children to sit in a circle.

What to do
Show the children the tambourine and explain that you will tap some sounds on it which you want them to count. Let them see the tambourine as you tap and count with them, counting each tap as it occurs. Now hide the tambourine from view and repeat the activity, counting with the children at first until they are confident with what they are doing. Keep the number of taps to no more than five at first. They may find it easier to concentrate on the sounds if they shut their eyes.

Questions to ask
How many taps? How many more this time? Are there more/fewer this time than before? Are there the same number now... and now?

For younger children
Use one, two or three taps at first. Tap the tambourine in front of the children so that they can count the movements of your hand.

For older children
Pass the tambourine around the group and let the children take turns in tapping the tambourine while the others count the taps. They can experiment with how many slow and how many fast taps they can count.

Follow-up activities
* Use a listening station and tapes of sounds which can be counted.
* Count the ticks of a hidden metronome.
* In movement sessions, ask children to change their movement for two or three taps on the drum.
* Children take turns to start and stop a tape of sounds for others to count.
* Follow instructions given by a number of claps: three means sit; two means stand up; four means hands on head.

Links with home
The children can play clap and count games with their family. If they have a chiming clock, the children can count the chimes.

Hops and leaps

Group size
Four children.

What you need
Photocopiable activity sheet 'Bunny hop game' on page 89, 1–6 dice (a blank dice with numerals written on by hand can be used), shaker, coloured counters or small cubes.

Preparation
Copy the 'Bunny hop game' sheet and give one to each child. They can colour in the pictures before the activity begins.

What to do
Ask the children to sit around the table, with a copy of the 'Bunny hop game' sheet and a counter in front of each of them. Together, read the numerals on the dice. Explain that they will take it in turns to shake the dice and move their counter that number of spaces along the track. The winner is the first one to reach the basket of carrots. Show them how to move on to the next square for the count of 'one, two, three...'.

Questions to ask
How many does the dice show? How many spaces will you move your counter? How many spaces have you moved? How many do you need to reach the carrots?

For younger children
Use a large spot dice with two faces, each with one, two and three spots. Ask the children to say how many spots when it is their turn. As they move their counter they count out loud the number of moves, counting 'one...' as they move to the next square.

For older children
Prepare a blank dice with other numerals, such as 0, 2, 4, 6, 8, 10. Read the dice numerals together then play the game. Ask: how many did you move? How many to the baby rabbits? How many more do you need to get to the frog?

Follow-up activities
∗   Play other board games such as Ludo and Snakes and ladders.
∗   Play 'Make three jumps, four hops' games in movement sessions.
∗   Sing the 'Counting game' song on page 85.
∗   Draw a hopscotch plan outside with chalk and play hopscotch.
∗   Walk or jump and count along a floor number track.

Links with home

Ask parents or carers to help the children to count as they move, such as counting the stairs, up and down, and playing counting board games.

Snack time count

Learning outcome

To count out given quantities.

Group size

Four to six children.

What you need

A saucer and plate for each child and some raisins in a bowl.

Preparation

Each child puts a saucer and plate in front of themselves.

What to do

Ask the children to count out seven raisins on to their saucer. Ask each child to use these raisins to count out four, five or six on to their plate in front of them. Encourage them to compare how many they have with each other and decide who has the same number as they have, who has more and who has fewer. They count their raisins back into the saucer then count out another amount and compare with each other. At the end of the activity they can eat the raisins with their drink for snack time.

Questions to ask

How many raisins have you? Who has more than you? Who has fewer than you? Who has the most? Who has the least? Who has the same amount as you? How many will you have if you take one more?

For younger children

Limit the number of raisins for each child to three, four or five at first. They can touch and move the raisins to check that all have been counted.

For older children

Ask the children to count out ten raisins into the saucer. They put seven raisins on the plate in front of them.

Ask: How many raisins are in front of you? How many are there still in your saucer? Do you all have the same quantity?

They should then put the raisins back into their saucer, and then choose how many to count out on the plate.

Follow-up activities

* Count out enough pencils for their group of children.
* Count toys as they are put away.
* Count out seeds to plant in a pot.
* Count out a given quantity of small toys into each section of the sorting tray.
* Make pegboard patterns using a given number of pegs.
* Count out a given number of Multilink cubes in a specific colour.

Links with home

Children can count out cutlery and plates for meals. They can help with cooking by counting out spoonfuls of ingredients.

Spin again

To count using counting skills in context.

Group size
Four children.

What you need
A cardboard spinner in six sections – six sections marked with random one to six spots, with a short pencil through the centre – a pile of counters or buttons in a shallow container, a mat or sheet of paper for each child.

Preparation
Put the counters in their container on the table with the spinner, and a mat in front of each child.

What to do
Explain to the children that one child spins the spinner and counts out that number of counters on to their mat. The others check the counting by pointing and counting. The next child spins the spinner and the activity is repeated until all have had their turn. They compare their quantities of counters and decide who has the most, the fewest, and whether any children have the same as each other. The child with the most counters at the end of each round 'wins' that time. The first child to win five times is the overall winner. When the game is played again, the child with the fewest quantity of counters each round can 'win'.

Questions to ask
How many spots on the spinner? How many counters have you counted? Who has the same number as ...? Who has the most? Who has the least? Who has more than ...?

For younger children
Use a spinner with the number range one to four and take the first turn at the activity. After each child's turn, ask whether they have more, fewer or the same number of counters as you.

For older children
Draw 5, 6, 7, 8, 9 and 10 spots on to a spinner. When the children have played the activity a few times, ask them to count out more or fewer than on the spinner. They check each other's counting for each turn.

Follow-up activities
✻ Play the following games: Dominoes; board games with dice or spinners; Snakes and ladders; Ludo; Picture lotto; Snap or other card games.
✻ Count sounds on a tape.

Links with home
Encourage parents or carers to play card and dice games with their children.

chapter five

Number

Numbers are in use all around us and children will see and hear them being used. Learning about numbers and number operations, such as addition and subtraction begins as soon as children start to count. In these activities the importance of developing mental strategies for handling numbers is stressed and expounded.

Picture card order

Learning outcome

To use ordinal language.

Group size
Four children.

What you need
Picture and numeral cards numbered one to ten.

Preparation
Stack the cards in a pile on the table, face down. Ask the children to sit at the table so that they can all see the cards.

What to do
Show each card in turn and ask the children to count how many pictures they see and say the numeral. Share the cards out among the children. The child with card 'one' puts it on the table, then the child with 'two' and so on until all the cards have been used. When they are confident at putting the cards in order, give each child one card to hold and put the other cards in order on the table, leaving gaps for the missing four cards. Ask each child where they think their card belongs in the order. The others check that they agree.

Questions to ask
Which card comes first? Which card comes after 'one'? What comes between 'two' and 'four'? What comes before 'three'? Which card comes last?

For younger children
Limit the cards to 'one' to 'four'. Ask the children to point to the card with one more than one, one fewer than three, and so on. Give each child a card and explain that they will put their card in order on the table, starting with 'one', then 'two' and so on.

For older children
Share out cards 'one' to 'ten'. Ask the child with 'five' to put that down in the middle of the table. In turn, each child decides if they can place a card before or after what is on the table, until all the cards have been used.

Follow-up activities
∗ Sing the 'Today's the day' song on page 87.
∗ Complete jigsaws with ordered quantities of pictures.
∗ Make pegboard patterns of one peg, two pegs and so on.
∗ Order numeral cards.

Links with home

Children can line up some toys and number them, one to five, point to 'four', one before 'three', one after 'two' and so on.

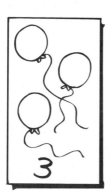

Tea party

Learning outcome

To count and find one more/fewer.

Group size

Four children.

What you need

Chairs, table, plates, play dough cakes or biscuits (alternatively, use large buttons or counters).

Preparation

Ask the children to put the cakes on a plate in the centre of the table and a plate in front of themselves.

What to do

Suggest the children pass the plate of cakes around and tell them to take three, four or five cakes each. Now ask them to each count how many cakes they have and say how many they think they will have if they take one more. Encourage them to check by taking another cake and counting again. They take turns to say how many cakes they will have if they put one back and check by counting. They replace all their cakes on the plate, then repeat the activity each taking different quantities of cakes.

Questions to ask

How many cakes altogether? How many on this plate? Put one more, how many now? Take one away, how many now?

For younger children

The children put one cake on their plate, then put another and count how many they have. Ask: how many will you have if you put one back? They check by putting one back and counting what is left. Repeat the activity for different quantities and for adding one more.

For older children

Extend the number range to six or seven, and repeat the activity. Ask: if you put one back how many will you have? The children then check by putting back one cake and counting what is left. When the children are confident with one more and one fewer, extend to two more and two fewer.

Follow-up activities

* Throw the dice and count one more than the dice score.
* Throw the dice and count one fewer than the dice score.

Links with home

When the children have a snack, parents or carers ask how many biscuits, for example, the children have taken, how many if they have one more, or one fewer.

Box game

Group size
Four children.

What you need
A box with a lid which will hold up to five bricks in a single line and five bricks.

Preparation
Show the children the bricks and the box. Ask them to check that the bricks will fit inside the box and that the lid will hide the bricks.

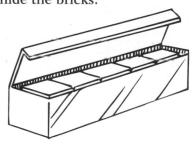

What to do
Show the children the empty box, then put in three bricks and put the lid on. Ask them to say how many bricks are in the box. Now add another brick without showing what is inside and replace the lid. Ask the children to say how many bricks are in the box. Repeat, taking away one or two bricks. Some children may find it helpful to point at the closed box and count imagined bricks in order to find how many more or fewer there are.

Questions to ask
How many did I put in? How many did I take out? How many are there now?

For younger children
Let the children put the three bricks in the box themselves and put the lid on. Shake the box so that they can hear the bricks move around and ask how many are in the box. Take the lid off and put one more brick in, but without the children seeing inside the box, and replace the lid. Ask how many are in the box now. Repeat for one fewer.

For older children
Count five bricks into the box. Remove two and show these to the children. Ask how many are left. Empty the box and then put in three bricks and then two more. Ask how many there are, encouraging the children to count on from three. Those who find this difficult can point at the closed box and count the imagined bricks.

Follow-up activities
* Add to and take away from a covered tray.
* Hold some pennies in your hands, then add some or take some away. The children count in their heads how many there are now.

Button sort

Learning outcome

To make reasonable estimates of small quantities.

Group size
Four children.

What you need
Assortment of large buttons (coat size) or counters, a large tray, plates.

Preparation
Put the buttons on to the large tray. Ask the children to put a plate in front of them. Discuss with the children the shapes, colours and designs of the buttons.

What to do
Ask each child to take a handful of buttons and put these on to their plate. They should estimate how many buttons they have picked up, then check by counting. Now ask one child to be an 'estimator' (or the one who makes the guess). The others decide how many buttons to put on their plates, keeping the quantities below five to begin with. The 'estimator' looks at the plates and guesses which plate has the most and then the fewest buttons. The children now check by counting. Repeat so that everyone has a turn at being the estimator. At the end of the activity they can sort the buttons by colour, shape or the number of holes.

Questions to ask
How many buttons do you think you have picked up? Are there more than five? Are there fewer than eight? How many did you count? Who has the most? Who has the fewest?

For younger children
Ask the children to pick up two buttons, without counting, and put these on their plate. They check how many they have by counting out aloud. Repeat for other small estimates, such as three and four.

For older children
Using smaller buttons, so that children can hold up to ten buttons in their hands, they pick up a quantity to put on to their plates. (Take care that the children do not put these into their mouths.) They guess how many they have and check by counting. When their estimates are reasonably accurate ask the children to pick up, without counting: more than seven buttons, fewer than eight, nine, and so on. They count how many they have to see how accurate they were.

Follow-up activity
* Take an estimated handful of counters from a feely bag, then count to check.

Links with home

When putting away the shopping, children can estimate then count how many oranges there are in the shopping bag. They can repeat this for other fruits and vegetables.

Three, two, one, ZERO!

Learning outcome

To use zero in context.

Group size

All the children.

What you need

The story 'Timmy's rocket' on page 82, numeral cards 0 to 10.

Preparation

Show the children the numeral cards one at a time. Encourage them to say the numerals. Introduce the word 'zero' and explain that it means 'nothing left'.

What to do

Explain to the children that you will need some of them to help to tell the story. Choose ten children and ask each of them to hold a numeral card and sit in a line, from 0 to 10, facing the other children. Read the story 'Timmy's Rocket'. When the count down from 10 to zero is reached ask the children with the numeral cards to stand and hold up their cards. After each number is said that child can sit down.

Questions to ask

How many children are standing up? Are there more than five? Are there fewer than six? How many are left now? How many are sitting down?

For younger children

Read the story but limit the count down from five to zero. Encourage the children to hold up five fingers and put one down each time as they count back until they show zero or 'nothing left'.

For older children

When you reach the count down in the story ask the children to hold up ten fingers and to count down to zero, putting one finger down each time as they count back. For zero, they can show a clenched fist, with no fingers showing.

Follow-up activities

* Using a dice or spinner which includes a blank section or the numeral zero, children count out the required number of counters.
* Read picture counting books which count back to zero.
* All the children can say the poem 'Little frogs' on page 78.

Links with home

When eating sweets, ask parents or carers to encourage the children to count how many sweets they have, until there are none left.

Collage share

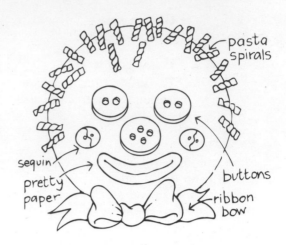

pasta spirals

sequin
pretty paper
buttons
ribbon bow

Learning outcome

To make fair shares.

Group size
Four children.

What you need
Collage pieces, such as pasta shapes, large sequins, buttons, pieces of pretty paper, ribbon, sugar paper for the collage, glue, spreaders, containers for the collage pieces.

Preparation
Prepare the table for collage work and put the collage pieces in the containers. Ensure that the number of pieces of pasta can be shared fairly between four children. The children put on their art aprons and place a sheet of paper in front of them.

What to do
Give out the pasta shapes so that the children do *not* have the same quantity each. Ask how many they have each and if this is fair. They put the pieces back into the container. Now ask one child to give one piece of pasta to each child, then again, until all the pieces have gone. They count how many they have and compare with each other. They should all have the same. Explain that they each have a fair share. Repeat the activity with the other collage pieces. Then ask the children to make a collage.

Questions to ask
Do you all have the same? Who has more? Is this fair? How many more do you need to have the same?

For younger children
Give out one piece of pasta to each child and explain that they each have the same. Give one child another piece. Ask: Does everyone have the same? Is this fair? The children can take turns to give out two, three or four collage pieces to everyone in the group so that they all have the same quantity.

For older children
Using cards or dominoes, share out the pieces unfairly to the children. Ask: Is this fair? Why not? What shall we do about it? Then ask a child to share out the pieces so that everyone has a fair share. Ask how they know it is fair.

Follow-up activity
* Make fair shares of snack time raisins, pieces of fruit or biscuits.

Links with home

Children can deal cards or put out dominoes, giving everyone a fair share.

Ten and beyond

Learning outcome

To name some larger numbers.

Group size

All the children.

What you need

The story 'Luke and the ten pound note' on page 83, telephone, strips of card about 30cm by 10cm, marker pen, £10 note.

Preparation

On the strips of card write the following: three three-figure telephone numbers, such as 999, 123, 345; three car number plates such as A123 BAT, B345 CHT, D678 EXL; three house numbers such as 53, 27, 100. These should look as realistic as possible.

What to do

Show the children the telephone number cards and choose a child to punch in the numbers on the telephone. Show the cards for the car number plates and for the house numbers in the same way and read these with the children. Talk about the children's own telephone numbers and ask individuals to punch their number into the telephone. Talk about the emergency telephone number and when this is used. Ask about their house numbers and family car number plates. Show the children the £10 note and talk about how much this would buy. Read the story of 'Luke and the ten pound note'. Talk about the large numbers in the story.

Questions to ask

What is your house number? What is your telephone number? What is your car number plate? Who has a really large number for their house? Who has a very small number? Who has an older brother or sister? How old are they? Where else do we see/hear numbers being used?

For younger children

Show the cards and ask which is the car number and which is the house number. Encourage them to talk about how they know it is a house number rather than a car number plate.

For older children

Provide pictures from magazines, scissors, glue and sheets of paper. Ask the children to cut out pictures with numbers in them and stick them on to their paper. Discuss the numbers they find. Say them for the children and talk about how they are used.

Follow-up activities

* Name coins, such as 20 pence, or 50 pence pieces.
* Use photocopiable activity sheet 'Numbers everywhere' on page 91 to extend the children's knowledge of numbers in the environment.

Links with home

Parents or carers can use opportunities where larger numbers are in use, such as birthdays, prices, distances and on advertising posters, to discuss these with the children.

Picture, tallies and numerals

Group size
Four children.

What you need
Sheets of paper, crayons, four sets of numeral cards numbered 1 to 10, small items to count such as toy cars.

Preparation
Put the items on to a table and ask the children to sit down.

What to do
Ask each child to take about four or five toy cars, and count how many they have. They should then draw a picture of each of their cars. Ask them to count their cars again and to count the pictures. These quantities should match. Show the numeral cards and provide each child with the numeral for their quantity, or if they can recognise the numerals let them find their own. Ask them to copy the card. Repeat the activity, this time asking children to draw a block or a line (tally) to represent each car.

Questions to ask
How many cars have you? How many pictures have you drawn? Are these the same amount?

For younger children
Use small quantities of bricks instead of cars, ask the children to count how many they have, then place them on paper and draw around each one. They count how many bricks there are and how many outlines they have drawn. Discuss that these are the same amounts and that each drawing represents one brick. Children can write numerals in sand to practise the writing movements.

For older children
Increase the quantities of toy cars for each child to eight, nine or ten. They count out the cars, then record using tallies and numerals. Ask them to check each others' recording by counting the cars and checking that these match the quantity of tallies and the numeral.

Follow-up activities
∗ Cut out pictures from magazines, stick them on to paper and then write how many there are.
∗ Trace along written numerals to practise number formation.
∗ Cut numerals from magazines and draw pictures of objects to match the number.
∗ Count sets of items on the photocopiable activity sheet 'Counting garden' on page 88.

Links with home

Children can play Snap card games with their family, where they match numbers and pictures showing quantities.

Card and board games

Group size

Four children.

What you need

Blank dice, photocopiable activity sheet 'Stars and moons' on page 90, counters, pencils.

Preparation

Write numerals 1 to 6 on the blank dice (or you could use a spinner). Copy the 'Stars and moons' sheet so there are enough for each child. Write a numeral, up to 6, on each shape (with repeats of some numerals on another copy) and photocopy one for each child.

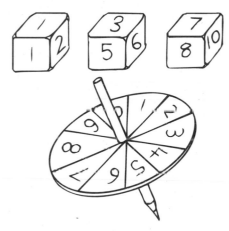

What to do

Ask children to read the numerals on the dice. Each child takes a turn to throw the dice, read the numeral and write that numeral on to a shape on their sheet. When they have filled all their shapes in one row the game has finished. For another game, give each child a sheet with numerals written on the shapes. Ask them to read each numeral. Call out a number. The children find that number and cover the shape with a counter. When a child has covered all the shapes the game is finished.

Questions to ask

What is this number? Can you find another shape with that number?

For younger children

Limit the numerals on the dice to two each of 1, 2 and 3. Ask the children to read each numeral and draw that number of spots in a shape. When they are confident at this, introduce 4, then 5 and 6 until they can read all the numerals on a standard dice.

For older children

The shape game can be played with a dice with 5, 6, 7, 8, 9 and 10 on it, or one with numerals randomly chosen from 1 to 10. When the children have written a numeral in each shape, they can play the second game, covering shapes with counters.

Follow-up activities

∗ Find a given textured numeral card from a feely box.

∗ Shuffle numeral cards, then place them in order from 1 to 10.

∗ Choose a numeral card then input the numeral into a calculator by pressing the correct numeral button.

∗ Use numeral cards to play number Pelmanism.

∗ Play Number lotto and Dominoes.

∗ Play board games such as Ludo, or Snakes and ladders.

Links with home

Someone at home can play traditional card games with the children, encouraging them to read the numerals on the cards.

Number search

Learning outcome

To use larger numbers in context.

Group size
Four children.

What you need
Real coins including 10p, 20p, 50p and £1, items for a shop with price labels of 10p, 20p, 50p and £1 attached, cash register, shopping basket, telephone, clock, calculator, photocopiable activity sheet 'Numbers everywhere' on page 91, pencils.

Preparation
Copy the 'Numbers everywhere' sheet so that there are enough for one for each child. Spread the coins out onto the table. Put the items for shopping into the basket.

What to do
Name the coins with the children. Show them the cash register and ask them to take turns in pressing the buttons for 10p, 20p and so on. Talk about shopping and the coins they would need to use to buy the items in the basket. Ask each child to choose an item, and match the price label to the appropriate coin. Talk about the telephone key pad and let them take turns to punch in a number. Similarly, children can take turns to input a number into the calculator and read a numeral from the clock face.

Discuss the pictures on the 'Numbers everywhere' sheet and ask them to join each picture to its number.

Questions to ask
Where is the five? What is this number? When would we use this? Where is the 'five' on the telephone? the calculator? What number is on this label? Can you find the coin to match the price?

For younger children
Use one pence, two pence and five pence coins, and some parcels with labels to match these coins. Encourage the children to take turns to be both the shopkeeper and customer and to 'buy' an item.

For older children
The children can cut out the pictures and numerals from two card copies of the 'Numbers everywhere' sheet and then play Snap with them. They 'Snap' for an exact match or for a match of numeral and picture. Similarly, they can play Pelmanism with one set of these cards, matching numeral to picture.

Follow-up activities
* Play shops.
* Make pretend telephone calls using two telephones.
* Provide some cut-out numerals for children to trace or copy.
* Read and trace the larger numerals on their copies of the 'Numbers everywhere' sheet.

Links with home

When out shopping, children and their family can look for examples of larger numerals, such as prices for petrol, house numbers, car number plates and bus numbers.

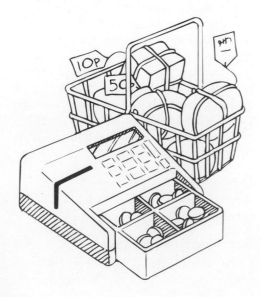

chapter six

Pattern

Copying, continuing and making your own patterns is the beginning of understanding about algebra. The following activities develop these ideas using everyday resources, including painting and bead threading. As a general point, it is a good idea to set up a display using the patterns which the children make.

Build an order

Learning outcome

To describe an order.

Group size
Four children.

What you need
Coloured building bricks of various shapes, with at least six bricks of each shape.

Preparation
Ask the children to unpack the bricks on to a carpet area on the floor and to describe them by shape, size and colour.

What to do
Put three different bricks in a line. Ask the children to describe each brick as you choose it. When the three bricks are in position, discuss each one, using ordering words such as 'between', 'first', and 'next to'. Ask the children to shut their eyes, then change the position of a brick. Can they see what is different? Build a tower using three or four bricks. The children copy the tower, choosing bricks to match. When they have finished, ask them to describe their tower and check each others' to see if all the towers are the same.

Questions to ask
Which is shorter? Is there a straight-edged brick? Is there a curved one? What is between the green and red bricks? Which brick is between the straight and the curved ones? Which is first? Which is last?

For younger children
Use coloured bricks of the same shape so that the only difference is colour. Repeat the activity, this time using colour language. Where is the blue brick? What is between the red brick and the blue brick? Which one is last? The children should copy your order. Then, one child chooses three bricks and makes their own order. They give instructions to the other children to copy: 'Put the red brick first, then the blue'.

For older children
One child makes a tower using five bricks. The others describe each brick, using words for shape, size, position, colour and quantity. Put five bricks in a line on the carpet, and ask individuals to change the position, for example: 'Move the curved brick to between the first and the next.'

Follow-up activity
∗ Repeat the activities using different construction kits.

Links with home
Someone at home can encourage the children to put three or four household items in a line then describe the order.

Painted patterns

Learning outcome

To make line patterns.

Group size

Four children.

What you need

Large sheets of paper, thick and thin paint brushes, paints of different colours, photocopiable activity sheet 'Line patterns' on page 92.

Preparation

Copy the 'Line patterns' sheet so each child has one. Make some regular repeating line patterns on paper, using both thick and thin brushes to give contrasts, and let them dry. Prepare a wall space where the children's completed patterns can be displayed.

What to do

Ask the children to run their fingers along the lines and describe the patterns. Then they make their own line patterns, either drawing the same pattern over the whole of their sheet of paper or making contrasting patterns. When they have finished their patterns they can use the 'Line pattern' sheet and trace the patterns on to the sheet, continuing the line patterns, then copy them in the space underneath.

Questions to ask

Which lines are straight? Which are curved? Which patterns were made with a thick brush?

For younger children

Use finger paints and ask children to draw line patterns with their fingers. They can make straight, curved and whirl shapes. As they work, ask them to describe the shapes they are making, using words such as 'straight', 'curved', and 'zigzagged'. If the children prefer they can paint their patterns on trays, then prints of their patterns can be taken on to paper when they are satisfied with what they have produced.

For older children

Place small quantities of paint of two or three colours into a tray, and put in two or three marbles. The children tip the tray, letting the marbles run through the paint to make line patterns. When the marbles have spread the paint, remove the marbles and ask the children to place a sheet of paper over the paint and press carefully to take a print. Remove the paper and ask them to describe the lines that they see.

Follow-up activities

∗ Use fabrics and wallpaper samples to look at line patterns.
∗ Use long narrow pieces of paper on which to paint line patterns, which can be combined to make display borders.
∗ Look for examples of line patterns when out for a walk, such as railings, lines of coloured bricks on walls and lines between paving stones.

Links with home

The children can look at the wallpaper patterns, curtain fabric and clothes with someone, for examples of line patterns.

Brick patterns

Learning outcome

To copy and extend a pattern.

Group size
Four children.

What you need
Coloured bricks.

Preparation
Ask children to describe each brick, using colour, shape and size words.

What to do

Put out four bricks, for example, red, blue, red, blue. Ask the children to describe each brick in the sequence. Explain that you want to make the pattern longer, so put down the next brick in the sequence, then the next. Ask the children to describe what the next brick would be, and continue the pattern, brick by brick. Ask them to shut their eyes, then make a new pattern, such as red, red, blue, red, red, blue. The children look at the pattern, describe it, then continue it. Repeat the activity, this time making a repeating pattern using shape rather than colour.

Questions to ask

What is first? What is next? What comes between ... and ...?

For younger children

Use beads and laces, and thread an alternating colour pattern, such as red, blue, red, blue. Put a threaded lace in front of each child so that they can make a direct comparison. Provide another lace and matching beads and ask them to copy your pattern.

Links with home

With their parents' or carer's help, using two or three types of coin, such as 1p, 2p and 5p, children make repeating patterns.

For older children

Ask one child to start a simple repeating pattern with the bricks, then ask the other children to say what comes next. When the pattern is completed, ask them to shut their eyes, remove a brick, close the gap, and then ask the children to look at the pattern and find the mistake.

Ask the children to watch while you make a pattern, and explain that you may make a mistake and encourage the children to correct the pattern as you make it. Make a more complicated pattern for the children to copy then extend.

Follow-up activities

* Make shape pattern cards, which children copy then continue the pattern.
* Thread some bead patterns which can be continued.
* Use construction kits or bricks to make repeating patterns.

Shape tile pattern

Learning outcome

To copy and extend an ABAB pattern.

Group size
Four children.

What you need
Mosaic or magnetic tiles or felt shapes and boards, photocopiable activity sheet 'Stars and moons' on page 90, coloured crayons.

Preparation
Copy the 'Stars and moons' sheet so there are enough for each child to have one. If the children have not used the above materials before, give them opportunities to play with the tiles before doing the activity.

What to do
Make a simple ABAB repeating pattern on a board. Ask the children to describe the position of individual tiles within the pattern, then to 'say' the pattern: circle, square, circle, square… Ask what the next item in the pattern would be. In turn, the children choose a piece to continue the pattern. Now they can each choose two shapes and make their own repeating pattern. Each child 'says' their pattern. When they are confident at making simple repeating patterns they can complete the 'Stars and moons'

sheet. The children copy the pattern in the space underneath and they can colour in the shapes to make a repeating colour pattern.

Questions to ask
What comes next? What comes before this? Which piece is first?

For younger children
If preferred, small toys can be used, such as farm animals or play people. Explain that you want to make a repeating pattern, and begin to put the pieces down. Encourage the children to 'say' the pattern. They predict what the next piece, and the next, and the next, will be.

For older children
Provide gummed paper shapes and sheets of paper for each child. Ask them to choose two shapes and make a repeating pattern, placing the shapes in line, but not sticking them down. They 'say' their patterns for the others to check, then stick the pieces to make a permanent record. They can make more complex patterns in the same way, such as AABAAB or ABCABC.

Follow-up activities
✻ Make pattern mats by sticking gummed shapes on to card, then covering with sticky-backed plastic.
✻ Do some alternating people patterns with children in line, alternating hands up, hands down, hands up…
✻ Do some individual movement patterns, such as hop, jump, hop, jump…

Links with home

Children can make ABAB, AABAAB and ABCABC patterns at home, using small toys or gummed paper shapes.

Printing

Learning outcome

To create an ABAB pattern.

Group size
Four children.

What you need

Items for printing such as feathers, sponge shapes, cotton reels, combs, small pieces of stiff card, corks, sponges, paints, trays, sheets of paper.

Preparation

Put a sponge into each tray and spread paint on to the sponge. This will help to ensure that not too much paint is used for each print.

What to do

Ask the children to choose two items to make their printed pattern. Encourage them to look at the shape that they are printing with and predict what the print will look like, then to print and check if they were correct. If using card, the children should print with an edge. To print they carefully place an item on to the sponge, then make their print. Then they repeat with another item to make an ABAB pattern. Ask them to 'say' their pattern. They can look at each others' patterns and take turns to predict what will come next. By using a mixture of items to drag, such as the feather or a comb, and items to print straight down on to the paper, they can make patterns with lines and direct prints.

Questions to ask

What is first? What will be next? What is between ... and ...? What shape will the feather make? What will happen if you print with the side of the cork? What shape do you think you will make if you print with the end of the cork?

For younger children

Using finger paints, the children can make handprint patterns, alternating spread and closed fingers.

For older children

Using long, narrow sheets of paper, they use combinations of items for printing to make a frieze for a display board. If the children work co-operatively to produce the same pattern, then the pieces can be joined to make the frieze.

Links with home

With their parents' or carer's help, children can look for and describe repeated patterns on packaging, such as stripes, stars, circles or checks.

Follow-up activities

* Cut out pictures of clocks and watches from magazines to make a repeating pattern.
* Make footprint patterns using finger paints.
* Make two colour print patterns, such as yellow feather print and blue cotton reel print.

Patterns in the sand

Learning outcome

To create a pattern from shapes and lines.

Group size
Four children.

What you need

Sand tray with dry sand, shells, pebbles, rakes, large feathers, spades, spoons, forks. If preferred, individual deep trays with sand can be used.

Preparation

Smooth the sand in the tray and put the items to be used by the tray.

What to do

Ask the children to make line patterns in the sand. They might choose rakes, forks or feathers. Ask them to describe their patterns, using words like 'wavy', 'straight' and 'curved'. They can smooth the sand then make a different pattern, using a combination of lines and objects placed in the sand, such as pebbles or shells. Ask them to describe the patterns they have made.

Questions to ask

What sort of line have you made? Which line is wavy? Which one is straight? How many lines can you see? How many objects are there in your pattern in the sand?

For younger children

If damp sand is used, ask them to make a sand pie and decorate it with shells and pebbles. Ask them to make a copy. Discuss how these are the same. Now ask them to make a sandpie which is different. They can make lines of sandpies, alternating their designs.

For older children

Children spread and print glue on to sheets of paper with a comb to make a pattern. They sprinkle sand on to the glue. When the glue is dry, they shake off the excess sand. Discuss the shapes which they have made and the repeats in the patterns.

Follow-up activities

* Make string patterns, sticking the string on to paper to make straight lines and curves.
* Use straws and blow paint to make 'dribble' patterns.
* Drag a straw through a blob of paint to make line patterns.
* Use a computer drawing or art program to create designs and patterns using lines and shapes.

Links with home

Using combinations of collections of 'treasures' such as buttons, sequins, pretty ribbons, children can make designs and patterns at home with an adult.

The music table

Learning outcome

To create a musical pattern.

Group size

The whole group.

What you need

Untuned percussion instruments, the song 'One, two, three, sing to me' on page 86.

Preparation

Put the instruments on a table. Ask the children to sit in a circle.

What to do

Sing the song to the children, then sing it again with them joining in. Sing it again, clapping the rhythm, and encourage the children to join in. When they are confident with clapping, give two or three children some untuned percussion instruments and they can tap the rhythm to accompany the song. Add more instruments, such as bells and shakers, as the children's confidence with playing musical rhythms increases.

Questions to ask

What comes next? How does the song begin? What comes after?

For younger children

Play 'Who is it?' Clap a child's name and say it at the same time, so that they understand how to play. Now clap a name and ask them to guess whose name it is. The game can also be played for identifying toys placed on a tray, or naming their colour, if preferred.

As the children become more confident at this, they can use percussion instruments to tap the rhythm, instead of clapping.

For older children

Set up a pentatonic scale with some tuned percussion (see diagram above). The pentatonic scale always produces a pleasant sound, no matter what order of notes is played. The children take turns to compose a simple sequence of sounds. These can be repeated to make a musical pattern. Encourage others to clap the rhythm or play percussion to accompany the tune. Their finished tunes and rhythms can be recorded for others to listen to. If possible, put a tape recorder and the tapes on to the music table.

Follow-up activities

* Sing along to tapes of songs with regular repeating rhythms.
* Sing songs and nursery rhymes with repeating choruses.
* Make up a tune and record it on tape.
* Make some musical instruments, such as shakers and scrapers, to accompany songs.

Links with home

Parents or carers may have karaoke type cassettes which children can use to sing to, and accompany themselves by clapping their hands or tapping their feet.

Step patterns

Learning outcome

To make an increasing/ decreasing pattern.

Group size
Four children.

What you need

Interlocking bricks in a variety of colours, such as Multilink or Unifix.

Preparation

Ask the children to sort the bricks by colour, then make sticks with the cubes, with each stick being a different colour, for example, 'one' could be blue, 'two' red, and so on up to five.

What to do

Make a staircase from the sticks of cubes, starting with 'one', then 'two' and so on up to 'five'. As you make the staircase, ask the children to find the next stick to go into the pattern. When the staircase is finished, point to a stick in the pattern and ask how many cubes there are, then ask how many in the one before and the one after.

Make the descending staircase in the same way and then let the children make their own staircases with the sticks of cubes.

Questions to ask

How many cubes in this stick? What comes next in the pattern? What will come after 'three'? What will come before 'five'?

For younger children

Use interlocking construction kits or shallow cuboid bricks to build a staircase. Let the children 'walk' a small toy up the staircase, counting the steps as they go. They could also make a double staircase, going up and down, and then count both sides.

For older children

Use construction sets with rods to build a staircase. If rods are not available, cut up coloured strips of card so that each strip has a clear number value.

Ask children to line up the rods in order to make a staircase. If strips are used, these can be placed flat on a table. Increase the size of the staircase up to ten, and down again.

Follow-up activities

* Make a printed step pattern.
* Make a bridge, with stairs up one side and down the other.

Links with home

As children climb up stairs with someone at home, they can count the stairs, and check as they come down again that the number is the same.

Play people parties

Learning outcome

To recognise cyclic patterns.

Group size
Four children.

What you need
Compare Bears or play people, a circle and a square cut from card.

Preparation

Ask the children to describe the card shapes and count how many sides the square has.

What to do

Choose four Compare Bears of the same size, two of one colour, two of another. Put the square shape down and explain that this is the Compare Bears' table and that four bears will sit at it. Ask a child to place a bear at the table, then another, until all four have been placed. The children now 'say' the colour arrangement of the bears. Ask if there is a pattern. If not, ask how the bears can be rearranged to make a repeating pattern of, for example, red, then blue, red, then blue.

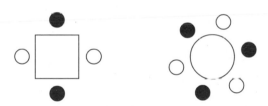

Repeat the activity using the circle shape. Increase the number of bears to six, then to eight. Keeping the same pattern used with the square shape, say it pointing to the bears, so that the children see that the pattern is complete.

Questions to ask

What comes next? Which is between ... and ...?

For younger children

Use the square card table and one colour of bears. Ask children to place the four bears around the table. Repeat the activity using two colours, and ask the children to help you so that a red bear is always next to a blue bear.

For older children

Give each child their own card-shape table and some bears. They make a pattern with the bears. Ask them to say their pattern. Ask if another bear could fit into the pattern. Remove a bear from a pattern and ask if the pattern still works. Repeat the activity with other arrangements of bears and using a hexagon card table.

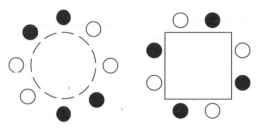

Follow-up activities

* Thread beads on to a lace to make necklaces and bracelets with a repeating pattern.
* Make people patterns around a table, arms up, arms down, arms up and so on.
* Play traditional circle games such as 'Ring-a-Ring o' Roses' and 'The Farmer's in his Den'.

Links with home

With their parents' or carer's help, the children can make cyclic patterns with beads, buttons and conkers.

Pattern

Decorated crowns

Learning outcome

To make a cyclic pattern.

Group size
Four children.

What you need
Paper strips to make the crown, sticky tape, cut-out paper shapes, glue and spreaders.

Preparation
Make a crown for each child which will fit their head. Stick the ends together with sticky tape.

What to do
Tell the children that the crowns are to be decorated with a repeating pattern of two different shapes. They can choose their pattern pieces and then place them in a circle arrangement on the table. Encourage them to check whether their pattern will continue around the crown. They can then stick the pieces on to the crown, again checking that the pattern goes all the way around.

Questions to ask
What comes next? What is before ...? What is between ... and ...? What comes after ...? Will the pattern go all the way around? Will the pattern join up with the start?

For younger children
They decide which shapes they will choose and make a random arrangement on the table. They stick these on to the crown (laid flat on the table) which is then stuck together with sticky tape by you. When they have finished, ask them to 'say' their design. Ask if any of the crowns are the same.

For older children
Encourage the children to make more complex patterns, with three or four different shapes. They place the pieces on the table, in a circle arrangement around the crown. Tell the children to spread the pieces so that they will fit the crown. Ask them to show that the pattern continues around the crown by 'saying' the pattern to the end and continuing it again from the original starting point. The children should stick the pieces on to the crown, being careful to keep to the order they set out on the table.

Follow-up activities
* Print cyclic patterns.
* Make Plasticine necklaces and bracelets with designs pressed into the Plasticine.
* Make cyclic patterns to decorate curtains for the home area.
* Decorate a birthday cake with alternating colours of sweets.

Links with home

Children can look at their mother's or carer's necklaces and describe the pattern checking to see if the pattern is repeated all the way around.

chapter seven

Sorting matching and comparing

Sorting, matching and comparing is an important element in developing mathematics for everyday life. Children will begin to learn about measuring, including length, weight and capacity. In learning about time, children experience sequencing events as well as using simple timing devices.

Dress to match

Learning outcome

To sort and match.

Group size

Four children.

What you need

A washing basket, a set of scarves, hats, pairs of dressing-up shoes and socks for each child in the group, a safety mirror.

Preparation

Mix up the clothes in the basket.

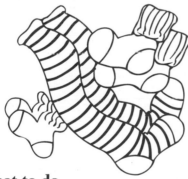

What to do

Ask the children to sit in a circle, with the washing basket in the middle. They take turns to choose something, put it on and describe it. Talk about each child's choice and encourage them to say why they made that choice. Put the shoes on the floor and ask each child to choose one and describe it. Hold up a shoe and ask who has the one to match. Encourage the children to use the terms 'match' and 'pair' when they talk. Repeat until all the shoes have been paired. Repeat the activity with the socks.

Questions to ask

How are these the same?
How are these different?
How are these similar?

For younger children

Ask them to look in a safety mirror and describe what they are wearing. They choose something for another child to wear and describe it.

For older children

The children count how many hats and scarves there are. They then check by matching that there are enough for everyone in their group. They can record this by drawing a picture of each child with a hat or scarf.

Follow-up activities

* Peg socks in pairs on a washing line.
* Do matching exercises: match each toy car in the garage with a toy driver; match the cars to lorries; make a line of red cars to match a line of blue cars.
* Play Snap and Pelmanism games.
* Provide shells and pebbles in the sand tray, and make some sandpies. Children put a shell on each sandpie. Ask them to make a line of shells and match it to a line of pebbles.
* During snack time, children help to give out a biscuit for everyone, and to check that everybody has a drink.

Links with home

Children can help to sort out the clean clothes, pairing socks, finding their own vest and pants, putting shoes into pairs.

My size

Learning outcome

To use comparative language of length.

Group size

Four children.

What you need

Large mirror, sheets of paper large enough for the children to lie on, marker pen, paints, the action rhyme 'Short or tall?' on page 80.

Preparation

Prepare a wall space where the paper outlines of the children can be placed so that the 'feet' of the outlines touch the floor.

What to do

Ask the children to stand in front of the mirror, in pairs, and to decide who is the tallest. Now ask each child in turn to lie on a sheet of paper while you draw around them. They can then paint themselves on to the outlines and, when these are dry, they can be cut out.

Secure the painted outlines against the wall, with the 'feet' just touching the floor. Ask the children to stand by their outline. Show them their reflection in the mirror and talk about how their height is similar to their outline. Ask the children to find someone else in the room who is about the same height as them, then to compare themselves in the mirror. At the end of the activity, say the action rhyme 'Short or tall?' and do the actions to show opposites of length.

Questions to ask

Who is taller? Who is shorter? Who is about the same height as you? Who has the longest outline?

For younger children

Ask two children to stand together, then ask the others to decide who is taller and who is shorter. Repeat this for other pairs. Ask the children to find two people who are about the same height as each other.

For older children

Ask the children to order themselves by height, starting with the shortest. They may find it helpful to compare their heights by looking in a mirror (if there is one large enough available). Alternatively, one child can be 'height sorter' and put the others into height order.

Follow-up activities

* Use finger paints to make hand and footprints and compare the lengths of these.
* Compare dolls by their height.

Links with home

Parents or carers can help their child to keep a growth chart, marking off their increase in height over time.

Teddy measures

Learning outcome

To order by length.

Group size

Four children.

What you need

Teddies of various lengths, strips of paper, scissors, large sheet of paper for recording, the action rhyme 'Short or tall?' on page 80.

Preparation

Ask the children to put the teddies on to a table.

What to do

Choose two teddies which are of different length. Place them lying side by side on the table, with their feet level, and ask the children which teddy is longer and which is shorter. Point out that the teddies' feet are in line so that the children should compare by looking at the teddies' heads. Place a third teddy in line and ask which is longest and which is shortest. Ask the children to put the teddies in order of length, starting with the shortest.

Now ask the children to choose three more teddies and repeat the activity. Check that they place the feet of the teddies in line. The children cut strips of paper to match the length of the teddies. These can be mounted on paper to record the order of the lengths of the teddies. At the end of the activity, say the action rhyme 'Short or tall?' and do the actions to use opposites in length.

Questions to ask

Which is the longest? Which is the shortest?

For younger children

Compare two teddies and talk about longer and shorter. Children may find it easier to stand the teddies up so that their feet are level on the table. Then choose two teddies which are similar in height and introduce the idea of 'about the same length'.

For older children

Put five or six teddies on the table together and ask the children to put them in order by length. Check that the children line up the feet of the teddies. It may help to use a strip of paper for the feet to be lined up against.

Links with home

Children can help with putting away the washing, sorting items by length.

Follow-up activities

∗ Sort out dolls' clothes to find the longest and shortest dresses and trousers, for example.
∗ Draw or paint pictures of three worms of different lengths, ordered by their lengths.

Big Ted is the longest teddy

Little Ted [ ]

Middle Ted [ ]

Big Ted [ ]

Pouring

Learning outcome

To use comparative language of weight.

Group size

Four children.

What you need

Dry sand, bucket balance, other items for balancing such as marbles, conkers, cubes, pebbles.

Preparation

Before the activity, give the children opportunities to use the bucket balance with sand. Place all the items on a table.

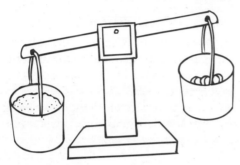

What to do

Invite one of the children to pour some sand into one of the buckets. Ask what happens to the other bucket. Now ask another child to pour sand into the empty bucket and for the other children to say 'stop' when they think both buckets have the same amount. Show them that when the buckets are level, there is about the same amount of sand in each one. Take the buckets off the balance and ask the children to hold them, one in each hand, and 'feel' that they are about the same weight.

Using some marbles in one bucket, ask a child to pour sand into the other until it balances with the marbles. Repeat by putting some sand in one bucket and balancing with some of the other items.

Questions to ask

Which has more? Which has less? Which is heavier? Which is lighter? Are they the same?

For younger children

Ask the children to choose an object to balance. In pairs, they can take turns to pour the sand while the other child watches and then says 'stop' when they are level and balanced. After each try let them 'feel' the buckets and ask them questions such as: Are they the same weight? Which is heavier? Which bucket is lighter?

For older children

Ask the children to pour some sand into one of the buckets, and then to balance it with some marbles in the other bucket (as in the main activity). Now they can count how many marbles they needed to balance with the sand. Ask the children to add more marbles to make them heavier than the sand. Take the buckets off and let them feel them. Ask them to check which is lighter, the sand or the marbles. Repeat the activity with other items.

Follow-up activities

∗ Pour out all the ingredients needed to make a cake.

Links with home

Parents or carers may like to take the children to the local playground to use the see-saw. They can talk about making the see-saw balance.

At the post office

Learning outcome

To order by weight.

Group size

Four children.

What you need

Various parcels of different weights and sizes including two parcels which are different in size but the same weight, and two parcels which are the same size but different in weight. A bucket balance.

Preparation

Set up a post office, with stamps for the parcels, money in a till, a telephone and forms to be filled in. The children can play as shopkeeper or customer before and after the activity.

What to do

Invite the children to take turns in picking up two parcels, holding them in their hands and deciding which one is the heaviest and which is the lightest. They then place the parcels in the buckets and watch the bucket balance to see which is the heavier parcel. Now ask them to find two parcels which are the same size. Ask if these feel the same weight, then the children can check on the bucket balance. Ask them to find two parcels which they think are the same weight and again to check on the bucket balance. When all the parcels have been compared in pairs, ask the children to pick up three parcels. They can then, in turn, decide which is the heaviest and lightest and again check by using the bucket balance.

Questions to ask

Which is heavier/lighter? Which is the heaviest/lightest? Which weighs about the same as this?

For younger children

Ask them to choose any two parcels and place them in the buckets. They decide which is the heaviest and which is the lightest. Let them hold the parcels and agree which one feels heavier and which lighter. Repeat for other parcels.

For older children

Put out four or five parcels, including two which weigh about the same. Ask the children to order the parcels by weight by picking them up. Ask them if any are about the same. Let them check their estimates by using the bucket balance.

Follow-up activities

* Pour enough sand into a bucket to balance a parcel.
* Order some bricks by weight and check by using the balance.

Links with home

Children can help to weigh out vegetables and fruit in the supermarket.

Snack time drinks

Learning outcome

To use comparative language of capacity.

Group size
Four to six children.

What you need
Jug with juice or milk, transparent beakers.

Preparation
Put the jug and beakers on to the table.

What to do
Ask each child to pour out some of the drink. Discuss how much they have in their beaker. Pour out a full beaker of drink for yourself. Discuss what happens if you pour to the very top of the beaker and then try to drink out of it. Ask the children how much there is in your beaker. They compare the beakers and decide which has the most drink and which has the least. Ask one child to drink until their beaker is empty. Pour some more drink into two beakers and ask them to compare to find which has more and which has less.

Questions to ask
Which has more/less? Which beaker is full? Which is half-full? Which is empty? Which is half-empty? Is it nearly full? Which one is nearly empty?

For younger children
Put an elastic band around each beaker. Ask the children to pour to the level of the elastic band. Ask: Who has more than ...? Who has less than ...? Move the elastic bands to mark new levels.

For older children
Pour some drink into your beaker. Ask the children to pour their drinks until they think they have just more than you. Compare the beakers. Discuss which beaker has the most/least, and which beakers have about the same.

Follow-up activities
* Use funnels, spoons, scoops and ladles to fill containers in the water tray.
* Make a jelly and talk about how much water you need to pour.
* Set up your role-play area as a café. Ask the children to pour drinks for their customers.
* Put about the same amount of cake mix into some baking cases.
* Pour out the same amount of sand or water into containers of different sizes.

Links with home

At home, children can help to pour out drinks and to make jellies. They can then talk about full, nearly full and empty when pouring and drinking.

Water play

Learning outcome
To order by capacity.

Group size
Four children.

What you need
Water tray, an assortment of sizes of containers including some which hold the same quantity of liquid, and some which are interesting shapes, scoops, spoons and ladles.

Preparation
Put the containers by the water tray.

What to do
Ask each child to choose two containers and fill them to the top. Encourage them to compare their containers and decide which one they think holds the most. Tell them to empty one container, then pour from the other container into the empty one to check which one holds more. Ask the children to choose two containers which they think hold about the same quantity of liquid and to check by repeating the method above. When they are confident with making comparisons, ask each child to choose three containers and to order them by how much they think they will hold. They can check by pouring one into the other as before and can refill containers from the water tray to recheck if their estimates were inaccurate. Repeat the activity, choosing from a selection of containers, scoops, spoons and ladles.

Questions to ask
Which container holds the most? Which holds the least? Which containers hold about the same amount?

For younger children
Encourage the children to pour from one container to another and to say which container holds the most and the least.

For older children
Ask the children to take turns to find how many cupfuls will fill a larger container. They can record how many cupfuls are needed by drawing the cups. When they have experienced filling one container with a cup, show them another container. Ask: Do you think this one holds more or less than the other? How many cups do you think this will hold? They can check by filling the container and then order the containers by how many cupfuls each one holds.

Links with home
At bath time, children can fill containers and order them by how much they hold.

Follow-up activities
* Order boxes by their capacity to hold bricks.
* Stack and nest some containers in order of capacity.
* Fill containers using plastic tubing and a funnel.

Photographs of us

Learning outcome

To sequence events.

Group size
Four children.

What you need
Four photographs of the children, including a photo of themselves as a tiny baby, sitting up, crawling, and now. Photocopiable activity sheet 'Build a tower' on page 93, scissors, coloured crayons, sheets of white paper, glue, the story 'Fosbury's day' on page 84.

Preparation
Prepare a copy of the 'Build a Tower' sheet for each child, and let them colour in the pictures. Be sensitive to any individual child's home circumstances.

What to do
Choose one set of the photographs and ask the children who they think these belong to and how they know. Now ask them to put the photographs in order. Ask which one was first and how they know, and to continue until they are all ordered. Choose another set of photographs and repeat the activity. Hand out the 'Build a tower' sheet and ask the children to cut up the sheet as indicated by the dotted lines. They should then spread the pictures in a line in front of them. Talk about each picture and what it shows. Ask them to decide which comes first, which next and so on, and to tell the whole story. When they have ordered the pictures they can stick them, in order, onto some

white paper as a record. Read the story of 'Fosbury's Day' and ask the children to retell the story in sequence.

Questions to ask
Which comes first? Which one is next? Which comes between this and that? Which is last? How old do you think you were then? What happens next?

For younger children
Choose one set of photographs and ask the children to pick out the baby photograph. Now ask them to find the one of the child sitting up. Ask: Which came first? Repeat for the rest of the photographs. Talk about each one in detail and how old the child was when the photograph was taken.

For older children
Cut up another 'Build a Tower' sheet and give each child one picture. Ask them to take turns to put their picture down, in order, and to tell the story as they go. Read 'Fosbury's day' but out of sequence and encourage the children to correct the sequencing of the story.

Follow-up activities
* Put sequencing tiles in order.
* Read a story to the children, then ask them to retell it in sequence.
* Complete a sequencing jigsaw.

Links with home

Ask parents to show children photographs of a family occasion. They can encourage the children to put them in order and retell the story of what happened.

Music and movement

Learning outcome

To experience different rates of speed.

Group size
All the children.

What you need
Tambourine or drum, cassette of different styles of music including fast and slow speeds, cassette recorder.

Preparation
Ask the children to get changed for a movement session.

What to do
Ask the children to listen carefully to the taps on the drum and think about what sort of animal might be moving. Start with slow taps. Ask the children what they think it might be. Suggest that it could be a tortoise, if nobody has already. Encourage them to move very slowly like a tortoise. Now make faster taps and ask what animal it might be this time. Suggest that it could be a mouse. Encourage the children to move much faster. When they have understood what to do, explain that you will make taps on the drum, and these will change speed. The taps will sometimes be fast, sometimes very slow, sometimes walking speed. Ask the children to move to the speed of the sound. Use the cassette of music in the same way. Play a slow piece of music and ask the children to move to it, and then repeat with much faster music.

Questions to ask
How fast is this? Is this one slow or fast? Is this one quicker than that? Is this one slower than that?

For younger children
Ask the children to move as slowly as they can, and then to move very quickly. When they understand what is meant use the drum to encourage them to move in time to the taps.

For older children
Ask a child to tap the drum, keeping a steady rhythm for the others to move to. Another child can take over, changing the speed of the taps. Ask: Which was the fastest? Which was the slowest? Now ask one of children to combine quicker and slower taps, and encourage the others to follow the speed of the taps.

Follow-up activities
* Compose some rhythms with different speeds using percussion instruments.
* Run toy cars down a ramp. Change the angle of slope to make them move more quickly or more slowly.
* Climb up a slide slowly and come down quickly.
* Walk 'on the spot' and increase speed until running 'on the spot'.

Links with home
Children can move in time to music at home.

All sorts of clocks

Learning outcome

To compare different units of time.

Group size

Four children.

What you need

Empty plastic bottles of different sizes, containers of different sizes, plastic tubing, funnel, dry sand and tray, sand-timer, some bricks, the rhyming game 'Mr Wolf's morning' on page 77.

Preparation

Fit the plastic tubing to the funnel.

What to do

Show the children the sand-timer and set it in motion. Explain that bottles and containers can be used as sand-timers. Ask one child to fill up a bottle with sand. Everyone watches as the sand is poured out. Another child chooses a differently-sized bottle and fills and pours out the sand. Ask the children to refill the bottles, and then to pour them out, starting at the same time. Ask which one took longer and which one was quicker.

Repeat the activity, pouring sand from a container into the funnel and tubing. The children try all the containers and find those which empty the quickest and the slowest. Ask one child to build a tower of bricks while the sand runs from the container they have discovered to be the fastest. Ask who finishes first, the sand or the tower-builder. Repeat for the slowest container.

Play the rhyming game 'Mr Wolf's morning'.

Questions to ask

Which is quicker/slower? Which is fastest/slowest? Which finishes first?

For younger children

While one child pours sand from a container, another counts to five. Ask: How much sand have you poured? Repeat while someone counts more quickly.

For older children

Ask a child to build a tower from bricks while the sand runs from one of the containers. Ask: how many bricks did you build? Repeat the brick-building using a different container. Explain that you want a really tall tower of bricks this time. Ask which container would give the longest amount of time. The children build a tower together until the sand runs out, and then count the bricks.

Follow-up activities

∗ Make a water-timer from a squirty bottle.

Links with home

Parents or carers can talk to their children about the different types of clocks and watches in their homes, and the numbers and symbols on the dials.

chapter eight

Shape and space

Shape and space includes exploring 3D and 2D shapes, position and movement, and reflection and symmetry. The following activities highlight the importance of making models and taking them apart to discover properties of shapes.

Where does it belong?

Learning outcome

To sort into a general set; to describe the sorting.

Group size
Four to six children.

What you need
A large tray, a large shoe-bag, small collections of items such as keys, beads, toy cars, coins and soft toys.

Preparation
Put the collections of items into the bag.

What to do
With the children sitting around a table, ask each child to feel in the bag and find something that is soft. They put their choice on to the table in front of them. Encourage each child to look carefully at their choice and describe it by how it feels. Repeat the activity for other sortings, such as finding smooth things, round things or hard things. Each time encourage the children to explain why their choice fits the general description.

Questions to ask
Where does this belong? Why does this belong in that set?

For younger children
Put the collections on to the tray and ask them to say what they can see. Choose a set, such as keys, and ask each child to pick a key and put it on to the table. Repeat this around the group until there are no more keys to be found. When they have put their keys back on to the tray, choose a different category, such as shiny things, and repeat the activity.

For older children
With the collections inside the shoe-bag, ask the children to take turns to choose something that is 'not soft'. When there are no more 'not soft' items left, the children replace them in the bag, then repeat the activity for another sorting, such as 'is not smooth', 'is not hard', 'is not round'.

Links with home

Children can help to put away the shopping, sorting out the tins, the boxes and the packets.

Follow-up activities
∗ At clearing up time, ask children to put away specific items, such as the scissors, the crayons or the bricks.
∗ Put out shape posting boxes for the children to use.
∗ Take a group of children for a supervised sorting walk, to find twigs, leaves, conkers and pebbles. They can tidy these away indoors by sorting them into labelled boxes.

Jigsaws

Learning outcome

To fit together and take apart.

Group size
Four to six children.

What you need
A jigsaw chosen from inset boards, tray jigsaws, lift-and-look puzzles, ordinary jigsaws, pictures from used greetings cards, pencils, scissors, envelopes.

Preparation
Offer opportunities for the children to play with the jigsaws before the activity. Choose a jigsaw which is suitable for the group of children and put that on a table with the cards, pencils, scissors and envelopes.

What to do

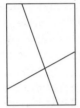

Take the pieces out of the jigsaw and ask the children to help you to complete it. Ask each child in turn to choose a piece and decide where it fits. When they have placed their piece, another child can check that it only fits in that way.

When the jigsaw has been completed, ask each child to choose a card, look at the picture and describe it carefully. Explain that they are going to make their own jigsaw. Show them how to make two cuts to make four pieces of a puzzle. Mix the pieces up on the table and ask the children to help you to do the puzzle. Deliberately turn pieces so that they do not fit and then ask the children to turn the pieces so that they do fit into the spaces. When the children have finished making their own jigsaws and then completed them, they can put the pieces into an envelope and pass their jigsaw to another child in the group to complete.

Questions to ask
Where does this piece fit? Will it fit another way?

For younger children
Choose a lift-and-look or a simple inset tray puzzle and complete it with the child. Make just one straight cut in the greetings card to make the jigsaw.

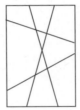

For older children
Choose a tray or ordinary jigsaw to complete together. The greetings card can be cut more times and with curvy or straight lines to make it more complicated.

Follow-up activities
* Make pictures and designs with shape tiles.
* Make pictures using felt shapes.

Links with home

Children can attempt more difficult jigsaws including 3D ones with someone at home.

Plasticine animals

To rearrange and reshape.

Group size
Four children.

What you need
Assorted Plasticine or play dough, tools such as shape cutters and rolling pins, craft boards or other table protection, a picture story book about animals, a table-top display space.

Preparation
Prepare the display space. Read the story to the children and show them the pictures.

What to do
Explain that you want the children to make animals from the story with Plasticine. Ask each child what they would like to make and to describe the animal. As they work encourage them to describe what they are doing. When they have finished their animal, ask each child in turn to describe their model to the rest of the group, using shape words such as round, curved and flat. Then ask children how they could change their animal, such as making it longer, more flat, giving it longer ears. When the children have described the changes they wish to make, they can go ahead and make them, and then explain how they are different from their first attempt. When the animals are finished they can be placed on the display table with the picture book.

Questions to ask
How can you change your model? Can you make this flatter/rounder? What is different? What is the same? What has been changed?

For younger children
Ask them to choose their favourite animal from the story, find its picture in the book and describe its appearance before making a model of it. When the children have finished their model they can describe it, and then use the same Plasticine to make a different model, describing and explaining as before.

For older children
Ask all the children to make the same animal from the story. When they have finished they compare their model with the others and describe the similarities and the differences, using shape language.

Encourage the children to describe how they could improve their model and then ask them to make their improvements.

Follow-up activities
∗ Make and reshape models with construction kits.
∗ Bake interesting shapes of biscuits and pastry.

Links with home

Children can, with their parents' or carer's help, make models from packaging materials and scraps of paper and fabrics.

Making models

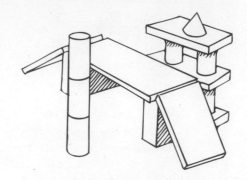

Group size
Four children.

What you need
An assortment of building bricks or a construction set including cylinders and spheres such as small balls, and cones.

Preparation

Choose a floor space where the children can work to build their models.

What to do

Explain that you want each child to build a model with some bricks. Give them some time to complete their model then ask them to describe what they have made. Encourage them to describe the shapes and properties of the bricks which they have chosen using language such as flat, curved, round, corners, pointed. Show the children a face of a cube and explain that it is a flat face.

Now ask the children to sort the bricks into different sets, such as those with curves, and those with flat faces. Encourage them to explain their sorting choices. Next ask the children to choose those bricks that they believe make good models and to build with them. When they have finished, pick up the spheres and cones and ask how these could be used in buildings. The children may suggest that these could be used as decoration at the top of their model. If cylinders have not been used for building ask the children to make a model incorporating them.

Questions to ask

What shapes have you used? Which shapes have curved faces? Which have flat shapes? Which shapes are good for building? Which shape would you put at the top?

For younger children

Remove the spheres from the set of bricks for this activity. Ask the children to sort out the bricks which have just flat faces and to use them to make a model. Repeat the activity, this time using just cylinders. When they have made these models ask how they could use the cones.

For older children

Set a challenge such as 'Make a tower as tall as you'. Ask the children to describe which bricks they will use and why. When the tower is finished, encourage them to draw a picture of it.

Follow-up activities

* Make models with construction kits and packaging materials.
* Make a train from large cardboard boxes.

Links with home

When out walking, parents or carers can talk about the shapes that can be seen in buildings they pass.

Sewing cards

Learning outcome

To describe patterns and directions of lines.

Group size

Four children.

What you need

Sewing cards and shoelaces.

Preparation

Make some sewing cards from stiff card. Draw around a template (shaped in any way) on the card, cut out the shape and punch some holes for sewing.

What to do

Show the children how to sew on the cards. Talk about left and right. Describe the movement of the lace, up, down. Ask the children to sew around their cards and to describe the movement of the lace tip as they sew. When they have finished, provide each child with another card and lace and show them how to make a zigzag pattern with sewing, moving from one row of holes to the other each time. As the children sew, ask them to describe the movement of the lace tip. When they have finished their sewing they can describe the shapes of the lines.

Questions to ask

What shape have you sewn? How did your lace move?

For younger children

Use simple sewing cards, with a few large holes. Encourage the children to sew with up, down movements. As they move the lace tip, ask them to concentrate on and describe the movement.

For older children

Ask the children to make their own lacing card pictures for each other to try. First they should draw a picture outline of their choice on to card and colour it in. An adult then makes the holes. The children sew their own card, and describe the line patterns they have made. They then undo the lacing, describing the movement of the lace tip as they go. They swap their card with another and repeat the sewing activity.

Follow-up activities

* Paint or draw line patterns: loops, zigzags, curves, straight lines.
* Draw line patterns using a computer art package or Roamer floor turtle.
* Drag lolly sticks through blobs of paint to make line patterns.
* Dribble paint from droppers to make line patterns.
* Run marbles through paint blobs on paper to make interesting line designs.
* Design a frieze to go around a picture using line patterns.

Links with home

Children can search for line patterns with someone at home on clothing, furnishing fabrics and wallpaper.

Shape tile sort

Learning outcome

To describe simple properties of 2D shapes.

Group size

Four children.

What you need

Shapes such as magnetic or felt shapes, or mosaic tiles, and boards; photocopiable activity sheet 'Shape pictures' on page 94, coloured crayons.

Preparation

Put the boards and the tiles out on a table. Prepare a copy of the 'Shape pictures' sheet for each child.

What to do

Provide each child with a small pile of tiles and ask them to sort out the shapes with straight sides. Repeat for shapes with curved sides. Ask the children to hold up a round shape, a shape with three sides, a shape with four sides, and to name them. Ask the children to find another shape which is the same as the one you hold up and then to make a picture with all the shapes. When they have finished their pictures, they can describe what they have made, using shape language.

Provide each child with a copy of the 'Shape pictures' sheet and ask them to find and name a shape tile to match each shape in the picture. They can cover the shapes they find with the tile, if they are of a similar size.

Ask the children to finish the activity by colouring in the shape pictures, using a different colour for each shape.

Questions to ask

Which shapes have four sides? Which shapes have curves? Where are the circles? Can you find me some triangles? Are there any squares? Where are the rectangles?

For younger children

Ask the children to use the shape tiles to make a picture. When they have finished, ask them to find matching pieces to the shapes they have used.

For older children

Ask each child in turn to shut their eyes then place a shape tile in their hands. Can they describe and name the shape?

Ask them to design their own picture using some of the shapes they have described and then draw it. Once they have drawn their picture, ask them to choose shape tiles to match the shapes and colours, if possible, of their picture and to make the picture with tiles.

Links with home

Children can look for mathematical shapes in the environment, such as rectangular and circular windows.

Follow-up activities

* Make pictures and designs using gummed paper shapes.
* Paint a large picture using just squares, rectangles, triangles and circles.
* Draw shapes using a computer art program.
* Find and colour all the circles and rectangles on a copy of the photocopiable activity sheet 'Counting garden' on page 88.

Printing

Learning outcome

To recognise faces of 3D models.

Group size

Four children.

What you need

Paints, sponges, trays, shapes for printing such as corks, sponge pieces, wooden blocks, paper.

Preparation

Put a sponge into each tray and spread some paint on to the sponge.

What to do

Ask the children to use the shapes to make some prints. As they use each shape, encourage them to print with each face, for example the end of a cork produces a circle while the side produces a thin rectangle. Ask them to look at their print and then at the face of the shape, and to compare what they see. Make sure that they can name the faces that they see. When the children have tried all the shapes, ask them to sort the shapes to find which will make triangles, squares, rectangles and circles. When they are confident with what shapes each item can produce, ask them to print to make a picture which includes triangles and circles, or squares and triangles and so on.

Questions to ask

Which shapes make squares? Which make rectangles and triangles? Which shape would you choose to print a circle?

For younger children

Use a limited range of shapes to print with, such as cylinders to produce circles and rectangles, or triangular prisms to make triangles and rectangles. Ask the children to predict the shape of the print and to check that they were correct. Repeat the activity over time and change the shapes which the children use.

For older children

Ask them to print with each face of the shape that they are using and to say how many faces there are. They can make a record for each shape on paper. See the diagram below.

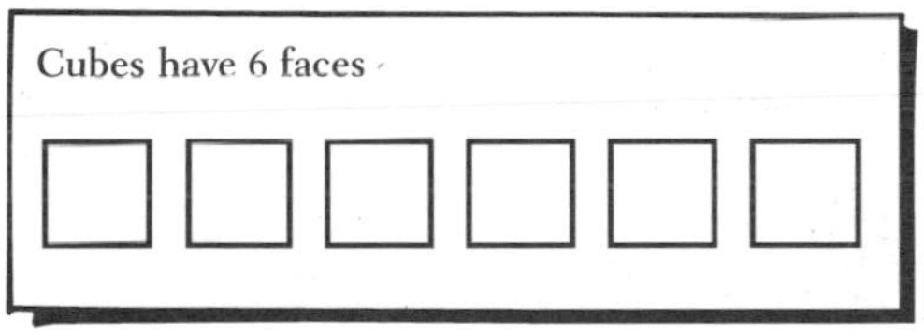

Cubes have 6 faces

☐ ☐ ☐ ☐ ☐ ☐

Links with home

In the supermarket, children can look at the way in which goods are stacked and describe the shapes which they see.

Follow-up activities

* Make a ramp and find which 3D shapes roll and which slide.
* Unfold packaging and look at the faces of the net.
* Cover the surfaces of packaging with paper cut to shape.
* Paint each face of a shape a different colour.

Blot and fold pictures

Group size
Four children.

What you need
Paint, paper, brushes, safety mirror, scissors.

Preparation
Fold each sheet of paper to make a crease down the middle and cut into a butterfly shape.

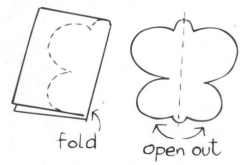

What to do
Open out the sheets of paper and ask the children what shape they can see. Ask them to choose some paint colours and to paint a design on one half of their paper, including some spots. When they are satisfied with their design, they fold the paper in half and press down all over the folded butterfly, then carefully open the paper again. Ask them to describe what they see. When the butterfly prints are dry, provide a mirror for the children to place along the fold line and to look at their print in the mirror. Ask what they can see. They can reverse the mirror in order to see the reflection of the other half.

Questions to ask
What is the same? What is different? How many spots can you see on this half? How many can you see on both halves?

For younger children
Before the children start to make their design, provide mirrors and ask them to look at their reflections and describe what they can see. This helps the children to identify what they see in the mirror and to begin to recognise it as a reflection rather than as an identical image.

For older children
When the butterflies are dry, ask the children to place the mirror on different parts of their butterfly. Can they see just one spot? or two? or six? Can they make the spots disappear?

Follow-up activities
* Use face paints and look at each others' reflection in the mirror.
* Look at the patterns in a kaleidoscope.
* Look at reflections in shiny surfaces such as bowls or spoons.
* Make designs with pegs and pegboards and look at them in a mirror.
* Make a printed pattern on one side of a line drawn on paper. Print the reflection on the other side, using a mirror to help.

Moving games

Learning outcome

To explore position and movement.

Group size

Eight children.

What you need

Large play apparatus such as a climbing frame, a slide, and a barrel; the action rhyme 'Moving round the room' on page 80.

Preparation

Place the equipment outside or in a large space indoors.

What to do

Ask the children to make a line behind an adult leader, and to copy exactly what the leader does. The leader takes the children around the area, turning, walking in straight lines, turning again and making a curved line. If possible include going under and stepping over small items on the floor. Now ask the children to find a space. Explain that you will give them instructions to follow. Call out instructions such as: 'Go up, over and down the other side of the climbing frame'; 'Go through the barrel'; Go under the bottom of the climbing frame'; 'Come down the slide'; 'Turn around and stand still'; 'Take three steps forward and bend down'. Ask children to suggest some movements. Finish by singing and moving to the action rhyme 'Moving round the room'.

Questions to ask

What moves shall we do next? Where did we start? Where are we now? How did we get here?

For younger children

Simplify the activity to one move at a time and encourage the children to really listen to the instructions by playing 'Simon says'. For example, 'Simon says: go up the slide. Simon says: turn around; sit down.'

For older children

The children can take turns to give their own instructions. Encourage them to use language such as turn, forward, backward, up, down. They can make the moves more complicated by combining movements, for example: 'Take three steps forward, turn around, take three steps sideways'.

Follow-up activities

* Dress a Roamer as a postman to deliver the letters around the room.
* Make the turtle in a LOGO program move on the computer screen.
* Sing action rhymes and songs.
* Give each other instructions for moving toy cars in the garage.

Links with home

When out for a walk, perhaps in the park, parents or carers can give the children instructions for moving. Confident children could give them instructions!

Models from pictures

Group size
Four children.

What you need
Picture cards of models made from construction kits, or simple but realistic drawings of models made from construction kits or building bricks, paper, pencils, crayons, photocopiable activity sheet 'Brick pictures' on page 95.

Preparation
Put out the construction kit or building bricks and the pictures/drawings. Prepare copies of the 'Brick pictures' sheet for each child.

What to do
Show the children one of the pictures and ask which construction pieces they can see in the picture. Ask each child to select one of the pieces. Using these pieces they take it in turns to contribute to building the model until it is finished. Encourage them to compare the completed model with the picture and check that they are the same.

Give each child a card and ask them to build their own model from the picture. Encourage them to choose all the pieces first. When they have finished their model they can draw a picture of it and compare it with the picture on the card. Children can use copies of the 'Brick pictures' sheet and bricks to make the models in the picture.

Questions to ask
Which pieces do we need? What shape is this? How many pieces do you need? Is the model the same as the picture? Is your drawing the same as your model?

For younger children
Provide a picture of a simple model, such as a three brick tower and use this to complete the activity. The models and pictures can become more complex as the children's confidence increases.

For older children
Ask the children to draw their finished model from two different views, then take it apart and rebuild it from their drawings. They can swap drawings and make each others' models.

Ask them to name the shapes which they can see on the 'Brick pictures' sheet and colour them in. They can then use the same colour bricks to make the model. This extends the activity to copying for shape and colour.

Links with home

Children can sketch their favourite toy from two different views.

Follow-up activities
∗ Describe shapes in pictures in a picture story book.
∗ Describe the shapes of buildings in photographs.

Mathematical skills

Name _____

Skills and concepts	Assessment and comments					
	Baseline/1st assessment	Date	2nd assessment	Date	End of year assessment	Date
Can use mathematical language to describe: * shape * position * size * quantity						
Can: * recognise patterns * make patterns						
Can: * sort objects * compare objects * put objects in order						
Can join in number: * rhymes * songs * stories * counting games						
Can: * count to 10 * read numbers to 10 * write numbers to 10						
Can use real objects to solve problems involving: * addition * subtraction						
Uses and understands vocabulary in solving problems such as: * add one more * take one away * how many altogether? * how many are left? * what will happen if ...?						

Counting to 10

Name _____

Skills and concepts	Assessment and comments					
	Baseline/1st assessment	Date	2nd assessment	Date	End of year assessment	Date
Can recite the number names in order.						
Can make comparisons of quantity.						
Can count items which can be moved.						
Can count the same items in different arrangements.						
Can count items which can be seen but not touched.						
Can count sounds.						
Can count physical movements.						
Can count out given quantities.						
Can count using counting skills in given context.						

Record sheet

Name _____

Activity	Page	Learning outcome	Date
COUNTING			
Circle time stories and rhymes	23	To recite the number names in order.	
Necklaces and bracelets	24	To make comparisons of quantity.	
Down on the farm	25	To count items which can be moved.	
Pennies and purses	26	To count the same items in different arrangements.	
Counting pictures	27	To count items which can be touched but not moved.	
Bird count	28	To count items which can be seen but not touched.	
Tambourine count	29	To count sounds.	
Hops and leaps	30	To count physical movements.	
Snack time count	31	To count out given quantities.	
Spin again	32	To count using counting skills in context.	
NUMBER			
Picture card order	33	To use ordinal language.	
Tea party	34	To count and find one more/fewer.	
Box game	35	To develop mental strategies for addition and subtraction.	
Button sort	36	To make reasonable estimates of small quantities.	
Three, two, one, ZERO!	37	To use zero in context.	
Collage share	38	To make fair shares.	
Ten and beyond	39	To name some larger numbers.	
Pictures, tallies and numerals	40	To record how many.	
Card and board games	41	To read some numerals.	
Number search	42	To use larger numbers in context.	

Record sheet

Name _____

Activity	Page	Learning outcome	Date
PATTERN			
Build an order	43	To describe an order.	
Painted patterns	44	To make line patterns.	
Brick patterns	45	To copy and extend a pattern.	
Shape tile pattern	46	To copy and extend an ABAB pattern.	
Printing	47	To create an ABAB pattern.	
Patterns in the sand	48	To create a pattern from shapes and lines.	
The music table	49	To create a musical pattern.	
Step patterns	50	To make an increasing/decreasing pattern.	
Play people parties	51	To recognise cyclic patterns.	
Decorated crowns	52	To make a cyclic pattern.	
SORTING, MATCHING AND COMPARING			
Dress to match	53	To sort and match.	
My size	54	To use comparative language of length.	
Teddy measures	55	To order by length.	
Pouring	56	To use comparative language of weight.	
At the post office	57	To order by weight.	
Snack time drinks	58	To use comparative language of capacity.	
Water play	59	To order by capacity.	
Photographs of us	60	To sequence events.	
Music and movement	61	To experience different rates of speed.	
All sorts of clocks	62	To compare different units of time.	
SHAPE AND SPACE			
Where does it belong?	63	To sort into a general set; to describe the sorting.	
Jigsaws	64	To fit together and take apart.	
Plasticine animals	65	To rearrange and reshape.	
Making models	66	To describe simple properties of 3D shapes.	
Sewing cards	67	To describe patterns and directions of lines.	
Shape tile sort	68	To describe simple properties of 2D shapes.	
Printing	69	To recognise faces of 3D models.	
Blot and fold pictures	70	To explore reflection and symmetry.	
Moving games	71	To explore position and movement.	
Models from pictures	72	To interpret pictures.	

Mr Wolf's morning

At 7 o'clock old Mr Wolf is getting out of bed.
get up from ground/stretch and yawn

At 8 o'clock he's growling 'cause he's gone and bumped his head.
scowl, growl and rub head angrily

At 9 o'clock he's drinking tea and listening to the news.
sip tea from cup and saucer/twiddle radio knob/hand to ear

At 10 o'clock he's bending down and doing up his shoes.
bend down and lace or velcro shoes

At 11 o'clock he's grumpy and he can't think what to do...
look grumpy, bored, puzzled/turn round and scratch
head/eye members of circle in a calculating way

At 12 o'clock he's hungry and he wants to eat...YOU!
turn round looking at members of circle/rub tum in a
hungry way/make a sudden pounce, leap or point on final word

Tony Mitton

The Game

∗ This can be played by one adult and one or two children, or it can be played by a whole group. The adult demonstrates how to act out Mr Wolf's actions and individual children subsequently have a go at playing the part of Mr Wolf.

∗ With the larger group, Mr Wolf can occupy the centre of the circle and do the actions as the others chant the words.

∗ Next, Mr Wolf can do one of the following:

1) chase the group, causing them to scatter, and the one he ends up touching/catching first is then the next Mr Wolf.

2) after a pause (indicated by the dotted line), he swings round the circle and points to one person on 'YOU!' who is then eaten and becomes the next Mr Wolf. (The victim could follow with a 'Me? Oh!' exclamation.)

Note: the last word 'YOU!' could be delivered by Mr Wolf only, or by the whole group.

Now repeat the game with a different Mr Wolf.

Little frogs

Ten little frogs go hop-hop-hop,
How many left if one should stop?

Five little frogs go hop-hop-hop,
How many left if one should stop?

Nine little frogs go hop-hop-hop,
How many left if one should stop?

Four little frogs go hop-hop-hop,
How many left if one should stop?

Eight little frogs go hop-hop-hop,
How many left if one should stop?

Three little frogs go hop-hop-hop,
How many left if one should stop?

Seven little frogs go hop-hop-hop,
How many left if one should stop?

Two little frogs go hop-hop-hop,
How many left if one should stop?

Six little frogs go hop-hop-hop,
How many left if one should stop?

One little frog goes hop-hop-hop,
How many left if *he* should stop?

Sue Cowling

Notes
i) The 'hopping' can be done by 10 children, while an adult and the rest of the group 'hop' with their fingers, holding up the correct number as a check.
ii) Start with any number, and ask the children to subtract more than one.

A tower of ten

1 brick,
2 bricks,
3 bricks,
4...........
5 bricks balancing.
Shall we stack some more?

6 bricks,
7 bricks,
8, 9, 10...
bricks go tumbling!
Shall we start again?

Tony Mitton

Notes

This action rhyme involves miming the stacking of building bricks.

∗ Hold your thumbs and index fingers of both hands slightly apart, as if holding small cubes.
∗ For each number add one brick to the imaginary tower, using alternate hands.
∗ After 5, draw back and look at the pile, holding hands carefully, as if the pile might be unsteady.
∗ Rehearse this section.

(This first section could be practised on its own, to teach the first 5 digits. The 'more' could then be understood to refer to yet another tower of 5, next to the first one.)
∗ Now start to add on the second section of 6–10. This time use mime at the end to suggest the tower toppling or being deliberately knocked over. Actual materials could be used. This will involve slowing the pace of delivery of the words, so that the speaking keeps in time with the action.

Moving round the room

Start in the corner by the door.
Crawl over the mat and along the floor.

Climb up on the bench beside the wall.
Walk straight along. Take care not to fall.

Jump down from the bench. Turn to your right.
Crawl in the tunnel. Pretend it's night!

Come out of the tunnel. Pretend you're a fox.
Crawl under the cushions*. Climb over the box.

Note: * could be 'chair'

Creep up by the wall to the door and then
Wait for your turn to start again.

John Foster

Short or tall?

Curl up like a caterpillar,
short and small!
Stretch up like a ladder,
tall, tall, tall!

Stretch out both your arms
to the side, side, side;
stretch out all your fingers now,
wide, wide, wide!

Swing back both those arms now
hide them by your side;
now you're only *narrow*,
not so *wide!*

Stretch up like a ladder
leaning on a wall;
reach up like that ladder,
tall, tall, tall!

Judith Nicholls

Squirrel store

1 nut, 2 nuts,
3 nuts, 4.
Squirrels go gathering
a winter store.

5 nuts, 6 nuts,
7 nuts, 8.
Leaves are falling
so they mustn't be late.

9 nuts, 10 nuts,
here comes the snow.
A scurry and a skip
and away they go!

Tony Mitton

How many?

How many pips in an apple?
How many currants in a bun?
How many chunks in a chocolate bar?
Count them one by one.

How many legs on a spider?
How many stripes on a bee?
How many spots on a ladybird?
Count them out and see.

How many bubbles in a fizzy drink?
How many stars in the sky?
How many hairs on a person's head?
Can you count them? Try!

How many fingers can you count,
starting off with ONE?
Count them out together.
Count them out for fun.
Ready? 1, 2, 3, 4, 5, 6, 7, 8, 9, 10.
(slow, steady finger-counting in chorus)

Tony Mitton

Directions
* Actors go foraging like squirrels, crouched with curled hands up to faces.
* For each nut the squirrels pick one up.
* Follow the poem's action.

Notes
* This is really a chanting rhyme, but it could be mimed and gestured.
* The final count to 10 is on fingers.

Timmy's rocket

Lots of strange banging and sawing noises had been coming from Timmy Rabbit's house for days. His friends were very curious.

'What do you think he's making?' asked Emily Squirrel. Timmy was always making things, but something usually went wrong.

'I don't know,' said Sammy Fox, 'But I'm going to find out.' He stood on tiptoe and peered through Timmy's window.

'What can you see?' shouted his friends.

'Something silver and very tall,' said Sammy. 'And it's pointed at the end.'

They all looked at each other puzzled.

'It sounds like a giant pencil!' said Marty Vole.

'Hey, he's coming out!' shouted Sammy.

They all waited eagerly as the door opened and Timmy came out.

'What have you been making, Timmy? asked Marty.

'A rocket to take me to the moon,' said Timmy. 'But I need some help to carry it outside.'

'I'll help,' said Sammy.

'And me,' said Marty.

'So will I,' said Emily.

They all hurried into the house and stared at Timmy's rocket. It was enormous!

'We'll put it in the garden,' said Timmy. 'Be careful you don't drop it!'

So they all carefully carried the rocket outside and stood it up in Timmy's garden.

'Tonight, when the moon comes out,' said Timmy, 'I'm going to fly to it in my rocket.'

'I bet it doesn't work,' said Sammy.

'You'll see,' said Timmy.

So, later than night, when the moon came out, all the animals gathered outside Timmy's house to watch him go to the moon.

First, Timmy put on his space suit and his space helmet. Then he shook hands with everyone.

'Goodbye,' he said. 'I'll send you a postcard from the moon.'

'It'll never work,' Sammy whispered to Emily.

Timmy pressed the starter button on the control pad.

'Now, you've all got to count from ten backwards,' he said. 'When you reach zero the rocket will take off.'

So they all started to count.

'Ten, nine, eight, seven, six, five, four, three, two, one...ZERO!' they shouted.

Boom! The rocket shot off, straight for the moon.

'He did it!' shouted Emily. 'Timmy did it!'

'Well, I can't believe it!' gasped Sammy. 'Timmy actually did something right for a change.'

'No, I didn't,' said a sad voice behind them. They all turned round to see Timmy standing there.

'I sent the rocket to the moon,' he said. 'But I forgot to get in it!'

Karen King

Luke and the ten pound note

Luke and his mum were out shopping one day when Luke saw a funny piece of paper lying in the gutter. It was an orangey colour, with writing and a picture of a lady's head on it. Luke picked it up for a closer look.

'What's this, Mum?' he asked.

Usually if Luke picked up anything in the street, his mum said, 'Put it down – you don't know where it's been!' But this time she stared in astonishment. 'Gosh, Luke!' she exclaimed. 'It's a ten pound note!'

'What's that?' asked Luke.

'It's money – quite a lot of money.'

'Is it enough to buy us a new house?' asked Luke.

'No,' said his mum. 'You'd need thousands of pounds for that.'

'Is it enough to go to Disneyland?' asked Luke.

'No,' said his mum. 'You'd need hundreds of pounds for that.'

'Is it enough for you and me to go to the pictures and have ice-cream in the interval?' asked Luke.

'I think it'd just about be enough for that,' said his mum. 'But we can't spend it, Luke. The person it belongs to might come back looking for it. We must hand it in at the police station.'

They went to the police station and a nice policewoman took down details about where Luke found the ten pound note. She also took his name and address.

'Well, Luke,' the policewoman said at last, 'if someone comes and claims the ten pound note, they'll be very grateful to you for handing it in. But if no one claims it in the next twenty-eight days, it'll be yours to do what you like with.'

Luke was very excited. 'How long is twenty-eight days?' he asked.

'Quite a long time,' said his mum.

For several days, Luke thought about the ten pound note. 'How many days to go now?' he asked his mum. But after a while, he forgot to ask, and eventually he forgot about it altogether. Then one day his mum said, 'It's a whole month now since we took your ten pound note to the police station. I suppose we'd better see if anyone's claimed it.'

And do you know? – nobody had! So Luke had his very own ten pound note to take his mum to the cinema. They had a wonderful time!

As they were leaving Luke saw a piece of paper under one of the seats – orangey-coloured with writing and a picture of a lady's head on it.

'What's this, mum?' he asked excitedly.

His mum looked round. 'It's a lolly wrapper!' she said. 'Put it down, Luke – you don't know where it's been!'

Sue Palmer

Fosbury's day

Fosbury the dog has a very fluffy face and floppy fluffy ears. He isn't a big dog, and isn't a small dog – he's an in-between-sized dog. His tail is long and waggy and his tongue is pink and licky, and he lives with a family in a house on the edge of town. His mistress is Beth, and she's six.

Fosbury's day starts in Beth's bedroom. He's supposed to sleep on the floor but somehow he always seems to wake up on the end of the bed! Every morning, Daddy comes in and says, 'Up you get, Fosbury!' and Fosbury yawns, stretches and trots downstairs.

He likes his morning walks with Daddy. Smells are fresher in the early morning, and the light seems clearer. When they get home, Fosbury has his breakfast, and then it's time to wake Beth. He does this by tearing back to the bedroom, jumping on her tummy and licking her nose.

Fosbury can't understand it, but most days Beth goes away to a place called school. Mummy takes her, then comes back and does things in the house. Fosbury sometimes helps, but he has lots of other jobs to do, like barking if anyone comes to the door, keeping an eye on next-door's cat through the kitchen window, and checking the kitchen in case anyone's dropped any bits of food.

Sometimes he has a little snooze, but he's always wide awake by three o'clock in the afternoon when Mummy puts his lead on and takes him to school to collect Beth. They wait at the gate, and when Fosbury sees his mistress he jumps and squeaks and pulls on the lead to greet her.

After school is walk time – sometimes Mummy and Beth take him to the park, sometimes Daddy gets back early and the whole family go in the car to the woods. Fosbury likes the woods – there are holes to explore, trees to sniff, and sticks to carry. There are smells of squirrel and rabbit and badger. Just the place for a dog!

After the walk, dinnertime: a big bowl of delicious dog food. Then Fosbury snuggles down beside Beth to watch TV.

And then bedtime. Beth has a bath and brushes her teeth, but Fosbury doesn't bother. He just goes out with Daddy for a late-night sniff and potters up to bed. And when Beth is fast asleep, he sneaks on to the end of the bed, curls up against her nice warm body, and closes his eyes. Until tomorrow.

Sue Palmer

Counting game

Johanne Levy

One two three, sing to me

Johanne Levy

Today's the day

With excitement

1. To - day's the day___ now you are 3___ Your friends are com - ing round for tea.___

Chorus

clap Hap - py birth - day, *clap* Hap - py birth - day, *clap* Hap - py birth - day Now you're 3.

clap Hap - py birth - day, *clap* Hap - py birth - day, *clap* Hap - py birth - day Now you're 3. To - Now you're 5.

Verse 2

Today's the day
Now you are 4
The postman's knocking
At the door.

Verse 3

Today's the day
Now you are 5
That's 5 whole years
You've been alive.

Johanne Levy

Counting garden

What can you see?

Count.

How many birds?

How many windows?

How many petals?

Count other things in the picture.

Counting pictures (P27)
Picture, tallies and numerals (P40)
Shape tile sort (P68)

88

Learning in the Early Years
Mathematics

Bunny hop game

A game for one, two, three or four players.

Use a dice and counters.

Start on the rabbit and finish on the carrots.

Hops and leaps (P30)

Stars and moons

Copy the pictures to make a pattern.

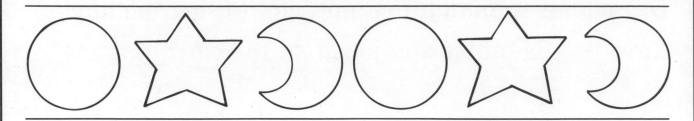

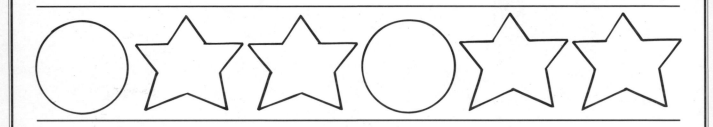

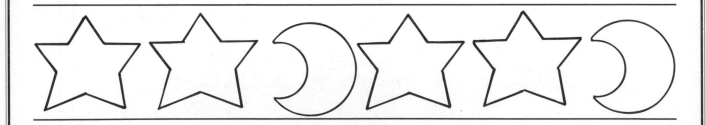

Card and board games (P41)
Shape tile pattern (P46)

Numbers everywhere

Where do the numbers belong?

Draw lines to match the numbers to their pictures.

Ten and beyond (P39)
Number search (P42)

Line patterns

Trace the pattern.
Copy the pattern underneath.

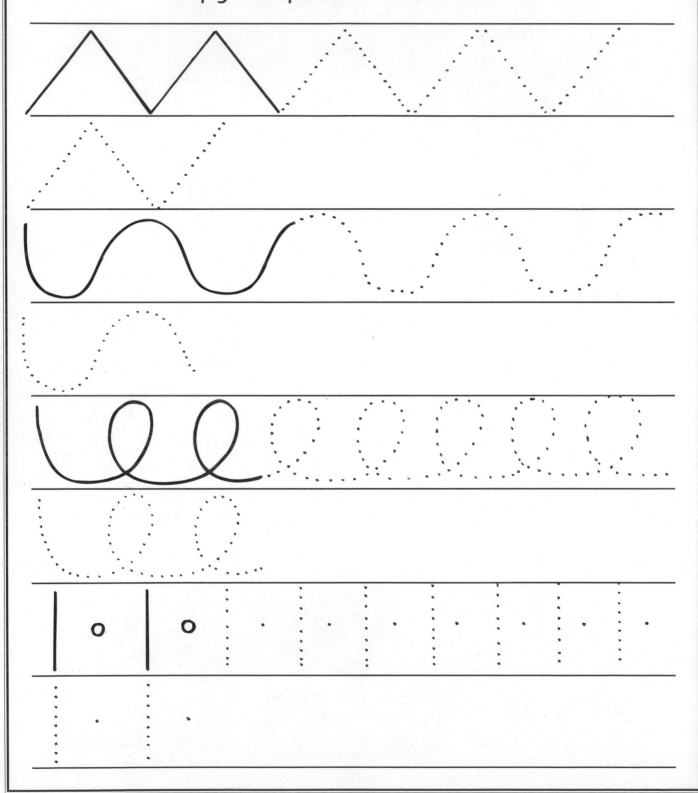

Build a tower

Cut out the pictures. Put them in order. Tell the story.

Photographs of us (P60)

Shape pictures

Find shape tiles to match these.

Make the pictures with your shape tiles.

Can you name some of the shapes?

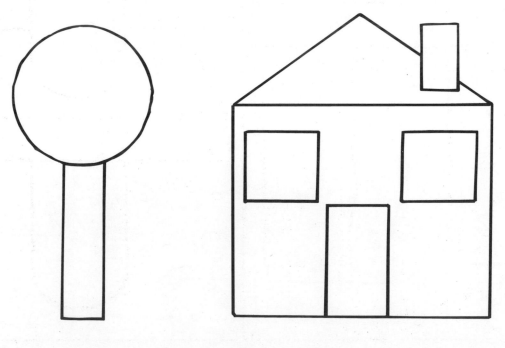

Shape tile sort (P68)

Brick pictures

Find bricks to match these.

Build the models.

Can you name some of the shapes?

Make your own models and draw them.

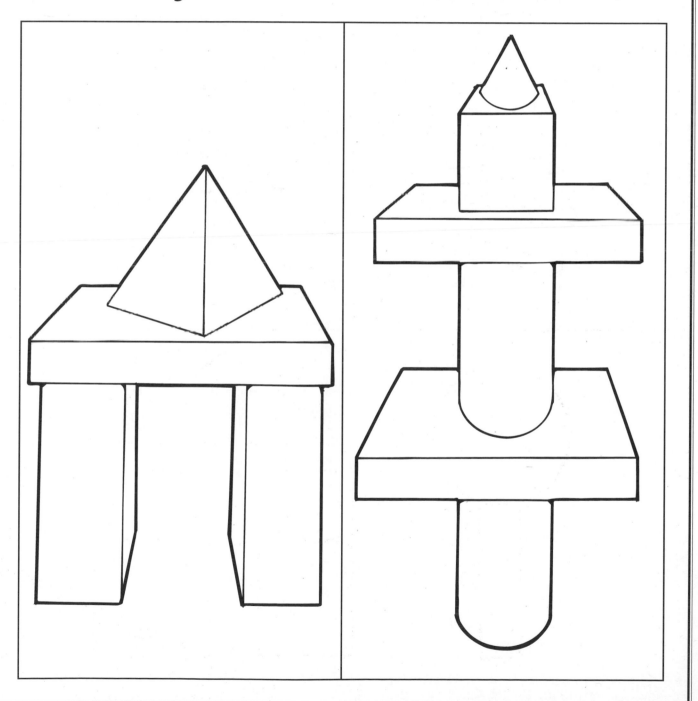

Models from pictures (P72)

Teacher reference books

These books are all easy to read with suggestions for how to approach mathematics teaching for pre-fives and ideas for activities.

Investigating Mathematics with Young Children R Althouse (Teachers College Press).

Mathematics for young children: an active thinking approach M Bird (Routledge).

A Desirable Approach to learning Mathematics Early Childhood Mathematics Group (BEAM).

Mathematics in Nursery Education A Montague-Smith (David Fulton).

Longman Primary Maths Nursery Handbook P Patilla, A Montague-Smith, P Broadbent (Longman).

Number books

These books involve counting.

Afro-Bets 1–2–3 Book Cheryl Willis Hudson (Just Us Books).

Lucy and Tom's 1, 2, 3 Shirley Hughes (Puffin).

Song and rhyme books

These books have some useful suggestions for counting rhymes.

Count me in 44 Songs and Rhymes about Numbers (A&C Black).

Clap your Hands Sarah Hayes and Toni Goffe (Walker Books).

Counting Rhymes (Ladybird)

Games and puzzles

Games such as Ludo, Snakes and Ladders, Snap, Dominoes and Lotto will all be helpful both in your setting and as suggestions to parents or carers to use at home. The following suppliers' pre-school catalogues offer a good range:

Galt, Culvert Street, Oldham, Lancashire, OL4 2ST

Hope, Hope Education, Orb Mill, Huddersfield Road, Oldham, Lancashire, OL4 2ST

NES Arnold, Ludlow Hill Road, West Bridgford, Nottingham, NG2 6HD

Computer software

The following software suggestions come from SEMERC whose address is:
1 Broadbent Road, Watersheddings, Oldham, OL1 4LB

The catalogue includes the My World Early Years software. This is available in Acorn and Windows format.

The following is just a selection of what is available:
Copy and Match; Early Learning; Jigsaw; Letters and Numbers; Me; Nursery; Shape Pictures; Sorting and Grading; Teddies; Visual Perception.

You can also obtain the following for Acorn machines:
Mosaic; Nursery Rhymes; Ted's Adventures; Toy Box.

Robots

Roamer and PIP are excellent to help children to begin to develop ideas of distance and turning. These can be obtained from:

Roamer:
Valiant Technology, Valiant House, 3 Grange Mills, Weir Road, London SW12 0NE

PIP:
Swallow Systems, 134 Cock Lane, High Wycombe, Bucks HP13 7EA

Useful addresses

BAECE and PLA produce helpful booklets on teaching mathematics.

British Association of Early Childhood Education (BAECE)
111 City View House, 463 Bethnal Green Road, London, E2 9QY

Pre-School Learning Alliance (PLA)
69 Kings Cross Road, London, WC1X 9LL

Write to the following address for a catalogue of other early years teaching resources:

Scholastic Ltd
Marketing Department
Villiers House
Clarendon Avenue
Leamington Spa
Warwickshire CV32 5PR